One Hell of a Paradise

One Hell of a Paradise

ANDREA VON STUMM

QUARTET BOOKS

Grateful acknowledgement is made to the Society of Authors
for permission to quote a copyright extract from
John Masefield, 'An Epilogue', in *Collected Poems*,
published by William Heinemann

First published in 2008 by
Quartet Books Limited
A member of the Namara Group
27 Goodge Street
London W1T 2LD

A catalogue record for this book
is available from the British Library

ISBN   978 07043 7123 1

Typeset by Antony Gray
Printed and bound in Great Britain by
T J International, Padstow, Cornwall

Contents

All writers are creative with the truth. The author allows her *alter ego*, Aleana, poetic licence to evoke certain periods of her life by relating events in a more imaginary dimension than the purely biographical.

PART ONE

Lugano

Help!

I used to drink to forget. Now I drink to remember.

I drink before driving because I drive better after a glass of wine. I drink to think, I drink to write, I drink before social events, especially one-to-ones, and actually in order to begin most of the things I should do. On the other hand, after more than a few glasses, I tend to postpone half of them altogether. Or else, I forget some item somewhere; I recall where it must be, then forget what it was. Carelessness is one of the most pernicious by-products of booze. You are seldom in a hurry. Purgatory can wait.

The idea of writing a sort of diary occurred to me at the airport. Would I remember that? I was too tired to read. My plane was delayed. It was seven in the morning. Sitting next to me, an American couple looked adrift. Her insistent stare made me shoot a frosty glance:

– What's the matter?

– You're so beeeeeautiful!

Since flattery gets people a long way with me, I smiled pacifically and inquired where they were going.

– To Madrid, she answered.

– To Milan, he muttered.

I went to the loo. When I came back, I wondered if they had agreed on their destination.

– To Chicago, they exclaimed in unison. It's just the transit we get confused about!

I knew how they felt.

– We flew the whole night from some place in the Middle East, sighed the husband, tossing his newspaper aside. I need a whisky-Coke to keep awake. Care to join me?

I had slept only three hours and any pretext went in my present condition.

– Why not? I replied, with a facetious hint of being merely polite.

So here we were, sipping liquor practically at dawn.

Not in the mood to tell my life story, I asked how long they had been married and how they had met: the unfailing formula to make couples talkative about themselves. Another classic: they had a heated argument about what colour dress she was wearing on their first date, what tune they danced to and so on, proving once again how subjective memory is in personal matters, and more alarmingly so in historical annals.

My flight was called.

– Off to Geneva?

Not an extra-lucid guess; it was the only flight boarding.

– You *look* like someone who'd go to Geneva! she twittered.

Thing is, I can look pretty well even when wrecked, and wealthy even when broke – a curse in disguise.

Just as well I was not the pilot. Not only because of the storm, but because even in the conduct of my life I lost the plot (no good premise for a real-estate agent like myself). Still: I can fool most people, most of the time. Modestly incorrect as it may sound, I am known to be intelligent and cultured, with the kind of charm which enhances looks not so very spectacular after all. I elicit sympathy, and failing that, curiosity. Why, then, am I the prey of self-destructive insecurity?

The one person I can no longer fool is myself. I need help.

What I never neglected, even feeling at rock-bottom, was fitness. Gym is a regular habit, eating little but well another, and my appearance is healthy.

But I was always shy underneath it all, and much less sophistic-ated than my nonchalance suggests. Initially, drinking helped overcome that fear of not being as witty and extrovert as friends I admired. To drink was synonymous with fun, and to gain acceptance. Now, it's become a palliative, just as smoking has turned into a nervous tic.

I have alternately lived in luxury, or counting every penny. My family was 'seriously' rich, then less so following their flamboyant bankruptcy in the 1970s. Some boyfriends were millionaires; some struggling artists; some con-men.

I married one of the latter, alas. He was a fraud and a rogue. Why did people trust him? Why were women, including myself, bewitched? He was no Adonis. In fact, he looked like a cherub; no sex symbol by any means, and my anti-type *par excellence*. But he was clever, quick, knowledgeable and, very importantly, he made men and women alike laugh – a lot. Most importantly though: his voice. I have seldom heard such a convincing voice. Can one fall for an organ in the throat? Yes. At thirty-three, I was tired of being 'available'. Cedric wanted to add an aura of respectability to his trade. I married a voice because I wanted a ring.

Now I shrug a cool shoulder, but being ridiculed by others was back then a contained nightmare in that I had kept my *faux pas* as secret as possible.

Ups and downs, sentimental disillusions, uncertainty, even betrayal, have taken their toll – and although I well know myself to be no exception, I am perhaps more hypersensitive and over-emotional than others. Genetically, I am prone to depression.

What definitely did not help was the menopause. It hit me with a big bang several years before the average age of fifty-one – a little over a year ago to be precise. First calamity: insomnia.

Who has never experienced this may not understand the pain and torment it causes. I'd take a tranquillizer to calm down, another at four a.m., when I invariably woke up, knowing or fearing I would not get back to sleep. The pills were harmless enough, I was mistakenly assured, but their very characteristic is that they get you hooked, psychologically as well as physically, possibly in equal measure. Worst of all: during this lapse of time, at dawn, comes an invasion of dark thoughts and feelings of guilt.

I wake up exhausted. It takes a bath, a coffee, noise (TV or music, don't care) to get into first gear. Then – especially since not bound by office hours – I wonder whether a small glass of cold wine couldn't lift me into second. Problem is: it does. Drinking has become an authentic disease. Because, of course, there are more gears, and more drinks to help switch into them. I'm a day-time drinker, let it be said, but Spanish days are long and I live on Majorca.

Another calamity: when in fifth gear, it is late in the evening or time to go to bed, and then comes the worst bit: I can't go back into neutral. I cannot switch the engine (my brain) off. So I toss and turn in bed, fighting the temptation to swallow another pill, but grow so enervated I usually give in and reach for one.

In short, I am not well.

Which is why I am flying to a country where some people have their money laundered, whereas I'll have my body cleaned and my brain washed.

In the plane, I thought of what my father told me the other day. He always chooses a seat near an emergency exit, be it on planes, in movie houses or wherever. My heart in some way shivered. I had no idea he thinks of such things. In his early eighties, he looks twenty years younger. He is a non-pedantic polymath, an enthusiast, and still quite a seducer! His sense of humour and twinkling eyes are indications of his quick-witted mind and his love of life. To me, he is immortal . . .

Over and over again I realize how ignorant one remains of the pulsations of even an intimate being.

Geneva

As always, I am amazed when, in this supersonic age, there are things that do not change one iota. Geneva airport is among them. Some nasty German made a fuss because of the long queue at the passport control: 'Wat iz zis? Ze zird world? Zis iz a unbelivigkeit! In Konzulat will I protestieren!'

He should have stayed in Gelsenkirchen, zat niuzanz.

It's so damn *neat* here – as opposed to clean, which of course it is too. This overwhelming impression of neatness, even though a bit annoying, being coupled with over-regulation in every sense, has something reassuring in contrast to the inner mess I feel trapped within. Everything has an air of decency and order about it. Most people wouldn't dream of crossing a street without respecting the zebra lines; lawns and treetops seem to have been trimmed with nail scissors; taxi drivers are not inclined to joke; and you can hardly walk twenty metres without hearing five different languages.

Switzerland is pleasantly familiar to me. I have lived here for some time on occasions, as related in two of my short stories, 'Double' and 'Quit'.

Anyway, having dropped my suitcase, I had lunch with one of my old friends, Lisa. She went into a severe and long depression after being the epitome of a balanced, strong and spoilt lady. Depression can be a rock: you stroll through life, and with subtle warnings, symptoms you minimize begin to accumulate, and all of a sudden it shatters you from head to heel, smashing the soul.

Lisa spent six months in a psychiatric clinic, of which she told me chilling episodes. She is well, or better, but somehow like a dimmed light. She even concluded that life – hers used to be a firework – has turned to black and white. She lost most of her money, her children moved abroad, and she became very fat, having been a Faye Dunaway look-alike. Her bloated face betrays years of constant pill-lapping: unable to face consequences, she retreated into a permanent half-coma. After an hour of wakefulness, another Stilnox would tip her back into oblivion. Escaping reality, she very nearly dug her grave.

The conversation wasn't precisely uplifting, but we talked as if we'd seen each other just the other day when in fact we hadn't met for years. Isn't that the essence of true friendship, and a reason to rejoice?

Still: to shake off the sense of malaise, I went to see a fantastic, clever and breathtaking movie: *Fracture*, with Anthony Hopkins and Ryan Gosling. The latter is told, at some point, to start worrying about himself. 'I've done enough of that,' he responds. 'Time to move on.'

A line to remember . . . on second thoughts a disturbing one. Are my problems the stuff of 'poor little (ex) rich girl' trash tales? All I know is that I'm drained, and that this kind of inner bleeding can turn to haemorrhage.

Even though I was tired to tears at this point, I wandered around for a while. At eight in the evening, half deserted streets, reminiscent of those in T. S. Eliot's poem, 'The Love-song of J. Alfred Prufrock'. What a contrast to Spain, where people live outdoors, bars are crowded, whisky and wine flows galore! Spaniards seldom get drunk, mind you. I can't remember which king enforced the wise law, ages back, that bars should produce something to eat in order to *tapar* (in this context, neutralize) the inebriating effects of alcohol: hence the *tapas* tradition. It doesn't prevent the Spaniards from talking far too loudly and generally all at the same time.

Like all drinkers, I also talk much too much. Very dangerous. The beholder of your secrets holds you hostage.

There are many reasons why I decided, on my own initiative and with fierce determination, to go to the place I am heading for tomorrow. Not least among them is to relearn silence and solitude. Apart from the damage inflicted on my nervous system by anxiety and booze (in whichever order), I have become addicted to background noise. One dramatically underestimates the brain deterioration caused by television. I believe that my sleeping problems have also been due in part to an overdose of images cluttering and cramming my brain.

There is another ugly component to my drinking: I can get

verbally aggressive. Rule number one, of which I have been aware all along, is to drink *only* when happy, celebrating or surrounded by the 'right' people. I transgressed that rule much too often, became depressive or offensive when deep down I'm a pacific, well-meaning person. Of all the things I need to figure out, this 'personality change' under the influence of alcohol is perhaps the most crucial. The detonator – there usually is one – igniting lucidity happened after Easter. Robin, my present husband, and his children had spent the holiday with me in Palma. The day they left, I didn't even wake up: I was too drunk. When I eventually did, I felt agonizing shame. It was dark outside and in.

Friday, 30 May
Still Geneva, then L. via Zurich

On my way to a business lunch, I walked for an hour. Everybody was heading somewhere with a strong sense of purpose, but without haste: the Swiss don't rush, no matter what the hour – or so it seems. They look earnest, but not preoccupied. I saw an advertising poster from the trademark Replay. Is replay going forwards and the point of therapy?

Someone saw me smile and looked puzzled, smiling without apparent reason being somewhat of an oddity here. I resisted the urge to gulp a glass of rosé: when it comes to work, I can pull myself together, and this meeting could bear some significant fruits.

I strongly believe in the adage according to which one is not given a second chance to make a first impression. Well: lunch was a success. (The sunglasses may have helped: I always feel obliged to be extra polite when wearing them.) Whether it leads to a concrete transaction only the future will show. My foremost objective right now is the one most urgent: self-repair. I am like a car with all its spare parts but an engine that short-circuits.

Time for a drink, I deviously decide, before getting aboard the train for Zurich. In this train it is impossible to open the windows.

I feel outraged, in a symbolic way, in what I'm representing as my last day of 'freedom'. Dependency being the antithesis of freedom, such choice of phrasing is blatantly fallacious of course.

I thought of my father (again), and of his expression 'I refuse to become the slave of my freedom', which always makes people laugh. It's his formula when explaining that he hasn't stuck to some resolution, like using his exercise bike or finishing a tedious book. Then I reread a letter he sent a few days ago, in which he tells me how proud he is I have taken this decision, and how confident. Warm words from a strong pillar.

Alcohol is a problem for him too, yet to a lesser extent, because my dragon mother keeps a stern eye, having thereby saved his life many times over, especially when driving. But he is too genuine an enthusiast not to defeat depression. When you were in Stalingrad, aged seventeen, relativity becomes second nature. He always warned me that one doesn't fundamentally change. At best, we learn to adjust our behaviour and goals to the knowledge infused by experience. Does that knowledge galvanize us with wisdom? On the 'exit only' lane, if that, he jokes, as a joyous spirit with a melancholy soul would.

An assiduous reader from an early age, I had the naïve arrogance to think this activity would harvest a short cut to some brilliant understanding of the world: nonsense. Spending half one's life absconded behind books doesn't make you streetwise or emotionally fit. It might turn you into a Nobel Prize, but I bet many of these have trouble hitting the ball. Mind-juggling with probabilities won't do, just as second-hand knowledge fails to prepare you for the improvisations and levity required to survive.

Someone I love in a very special way met me at the Zurich station. As we hugged, an overwhelming feeling overcame me like a tide: Hugo will always be there if I need him. It hasn't always been so. He is not known for reliability.

We lived together (or was it side by side?) in Geneva in the early nineties. In many ways, he sabotaged my innocence. I counted on every promise he made. Starry eyed, I shared every dream he elaborated. His baroque, romantic fantasy, his desultory sincerity, his sense of humour cemented a profound and tender bond between us. While knowing his intelligence to be extravagant – though ignoring it was just as utopian – I believed every word he said.

Yet he lied to me, and not just for bagatelles. Besides being distraught and disappointed, I felt unjustly insulted. All of that initiated a period of excessive drinking, which culminated in what for the moment I shall call, for lack of courage, an Accident, capital A.

Having said this, I left him twice to seek solace in other arms, but came back to find his wide open, my despicable behaviour notwithstanding. In spite or because of it all, he was what one calls *un grand amour*.

Last-minute shopping. Toothpaste, earplugs, body lotion and, most importantly, an eye mask, like the ones they give out on planes. Will there be shutters where I'm going? Iron bars? The truth is I hardly know anything about the place. The brochure gave little away, neither in terms of pictures, nor about the pro-gramme, the therapy and so on. I only know the setting is beautiful. Finally to call the truth by name, I am checking into a psychiatric clinic. Lisa's descriptions of the one she went to were grim: they searched her, removed anything with a cutting edge and allocated her a room she had to share with a perfect stranger. Furthermore, in order to break off all contact with the outside world, they confiscated her cell phone, her computer, even her alarm clock.

Do people freak out when isolated? Could the wrong room-mate exacerbate one's blues? I am over-aware, even though scared, of the privilege, in terms of money and time, of being able to seek medical help and psychological support.

Hugo offering to take me there – a five-hour-long drive (and for him, the same distance back) with nervous me at his side, unlikely to provide scintillating conversation – is the biggest present he could have given. But he is witty enough for two, mostly in a 'second-degree' way.

Tonight, in Lugano, I shall gulp down a whole bottle of wine. *The last one*.

About thirty years ago, the most gracious, amusing, stunning lady I ever knew joked: 'I don't have friends, I only have drinking companions.' She is now an AA, in retreat on some Aeolian island, having severed most links with her previous life. From what I have heard, she has also discarded men. Not an option!

Last but not least: my decision has another crucial aspect. I want to protect my (second and last) marriage. Should I endanger that, I will have torpedoed my life.

Some of Hugo's words:

- I stopped drinking years ago, and do you know what? I was disappointed. It was too easy!
- You shouldn't be apprehensive (I had told him about my panic attack when I packed my suitcase in Palma). What you are about to strive for is simple. You will succeed. I may know you better than you do.
- Relationships shouldn't be idealized: they don't work (this said without sarcasm).
- The main purpose of intelligence is self-preservation. What you have decided is to protect yourself.
- After you come out, do not punish others because you experience hardship. Don't worry: you'll be in the best mood, because you'll feel so much better. Life being a mirror, hold your head up.
- Remember the saying, 'I am me and my circumstances'? Well. The 'watchers' believe in luck and circumstances. The 'doers' believe in causes and effects
- You're a beauty and a beast, and I respect both.
- Attitudes are more important than aptitudes, and, among

the most vital ones, laughter is a bullet-proof jacket. Wits are useless without a talent for self-derision.

- I don't waste time any more sharpening a pencil until its tip is perfect; sooner or later it will break. Perfection is not the objective.
- Beware of sadness as it can become a vicious habit.

Needless to say, all these remarks were sprinkled across hours of driving and then dining. Hugo does not pontificate, neither does he judge. Yet the last thing he said was:

– Avoid people who can hurt you, and beware of your mother, to begin with. I remember her as a sort of omniscient eagle hovering above you – and you, *mon chou*, have a lot of unlearning to do.

When we parted, I sobbed as discreetly as possible, wishing to be a kid holding on to a protecting hand. As not being a kid any longer was no bigger a scoop than being on one's own, I did not turn to wave goodbye.

Ascending the steep stairs (a symbol?) to the clinic's entrance, I was no longer afraid. If character is destiny, as I am convinced it is, I could walk through the door intent on reinforcing mine for the better. Be that as it may: trial-and-error has, at this juncture, hurled me into a hit-and-run situation, heading for a dead-end street. No good when feeling stymied by a surplus of empirical imagination. I need to stop for a while, engine turned off.

Arrival

This is not at all as I expected.

The place is wonderful. It almost gives the impression of a *pension de famille*. Downstairs, two sitting rooms, one for smokers, with a music console and newspapers; another for non-smokers with a television, a bridge table, comfortable sofas and rugs. There are no more than forty-five rooms, all individual. Mine has a balcony overlooking the picturesque garden, a patch of lake, the town and the mountains. Its furnishings, however, are definitely hospital-like. But it is spacious, has bay windows and – and – a bathtub!

I was taken to a study and asked very few questions by Dottore M and Dottoressa D, the two psychiatrists who will be following me throughout my stay. I liked them at once. I think they liked me too, perhaps because I don't beat about the bush. I have lied too much in my life; it is restful to cease. They must also have sensed my genuine despair.

No luggage examination. All they asked is that I hand over whatever medication I had. I did, and that was that. To my following amazement, they offered to connect a TV. I declined. It is peace and isolation I seek: precisely what the philosophy here seems to be all about. No collective dining room (meals are brought to one's room), no regimented time schedule, no bosomy matrons casting severe glances from behind bespectacled eyes. What a relief! I had hesitated between this clinic, and the one near Geneva Lisa went to. It was too expensive for one thing, and I didn't want to be too close to Hugo or familiar surroundings. Also, the regulations she had described sounded punishing: group therapy from dawn to dusk; hardly half an hour spare between obligatory activities. With laundry and ironing to be done by the patient, there would hardly have been a moment's peace and quiet. Every institution has its credo. Here, the programme is drawn according to each patient's condition. The nurses are young and cheerful; laundry is charged but available. There is even a telephone booth. As a cherry on the cake, I'm allowed my PC, have turned the table towards the view and promised not to use the Internet. That was the condition. They trusted my promise.

Only half unpacked, I was given an intravenous infusion lasting one hour. They call it Phlebo. It is a mixture of sedatives, minerals, vitamins, primarily meant to clean your blood.

I cried during the whole duration. Don't know why. Tears just rolled down my cheeks, uncontrollably. Perhaps this was a first symptom of 'letting go'. I also froze in spite of the mild temperature – a premature symptom of withdrawal? Unlikely, since a scan of my body wouldn't look very different from that of a wine cellar. What I am, right now, is utterly and completely exhausted.

They advised I continued lying down, but my nerves wouldn't let me. So I went downstairs, to the smoking salon.

The windows were open, a soothing breeze sweeping the air, and no one else was around other than a man whose eyes seemed to pierce mine. He at once redirected his X-ray sight on to a voluminous bundle of sheets and hummed an aria I recognized but could not place in context. The way the man looked at me had in no way been disturbing: his were eyes of an intense goodness. He seemed to radiate almost a saintly aura. His tonsure might have helped convey this impression, along with his black djellaba, but there was more to it . . . His craggy peasant's face contrasted with long, delicate hands, from which dropped several sheets of paper. He was reading music staves, and singing what he read! Evidently he was immured in a world of his own, so I kept quiet and picked up an Italian paper.

The first article I came across was, oh surprise, about

dependency. Mainly because of the inevitable parallels to ethylic abuse, it mobilized my attention. In résumé it ran:

Easy Way to Stop Smoking, Allen Carr's bestseller – eight million copies sold worldwide and translated into dozens of languages – claims that quitting his consumption after about a hundred cigarettes daily saved his life. (In Spain, where I live, they say, what the hell, smoking may cause death, but living kills for sure!) Carr nevertheless died of lung cancer thirty years later. Might that discourage his disciples?

Most smokers say that could they turn the clock back, they would never start; seventy per cent admit they would stop if they only could. Few are those who manage to moderate their intake. Reducing a vice to a controlled pleasure is a next to impossible mission, abstinence often being accompanied by weight gain, insomnia, anxiety, lack of concentration, etc.

The consequence: less than five per cent of smokers consuming twenty cigarettes or more succeed, if data from the Food and Drug Administration is correct.

Amazingly, about half of the smokers who undergo lung – even larynx – surgery, start again. Psychiatric or pharmaceutical (such as Bupriopion or Zybac) support fails in seventy per cent of cases, smokers relapsing on average after one week of abstinence. Patches or sprays fare no better.

(What underlies my hope that alcohol addiction can be shaken off more easily is the chemical manipulation tobacco multinationals still manage to get away with: nicotine in itself is addictive, even though the organisms of non-smokers produce it to some degree, meaning the body needs a minimal dose.) The substances that get added to cigarettes are staggering: to increase the physiological need, tobacco is mixed with a composite that not only accelerates the release of nicotine into the blood but also dilates the lungs, facilitating the poison's absorption. A vaccine against tobacco dependency is being tested: Veriniclin, a pill that fools the brain into believing it has received its 'kick', has recently been marketed, but who knows with what long-term side-effects?

Thank God, the fag producers' outrageous manoeuvres are not possible with wine. (Is it with other liquors? No idea.) On the other hand, cigarettes do not act as mind-altering disinhibitors. (What the article did not say is that five out of the first six Nobel Prize Winners for Literature were alcoholics – a fact – and presumably also smokers!)

According to a study by the American medical magazine *Bmc genetics*, the ability to 'kill the habit' depends on the presence of 221 genes, or lack thereof. Is willpower – the real issue, when all is said but not done – a lottery?

When I looked up from reading, the 'Music Monk' had disappeared. I went out to the garden and sat on a bench. I felt like crying again and would probably have done so had I not been joined by a lovely, talkative girl introducing herself as Tonia. She told me why she was in the clinic, probably to distract me, for she had felt how I was feeling as I sensed her empathy.

A handsome forty-year-old, she had rebounded into multiple drug addiction – after ten years clear. She is bright and vivacious, quite pretty too. Her room is in a separate secure annex I hadn't realized existed in these grounds. There you are shut up at night, windows are barred and your bathroom is locked; common meals are served with plastic cutlery, lights controlled by a central switchboard, and so on. I have been wondering where the psychotic, schizophrenic and hyper-something-or-other patients were. Now I know. During daytime, however, they come to the main building and participate in activities based on art and music, or watch TV.

Later on, it was explained to me what medication I would be given: in the morning an antidepressant and high doses of magnesium and vitamins, especially of the B sort; at noon a hormone-balancing pill and one against abstinence symptoms; and before sleeping, an intravenous infusion similar to the one I received earlier.

As far as I was concerned, they could feed me stones; I would have swallowed them unturned. I would do as I was told. That is what I came here for.

Everything here is human, warm and conducive to inner peace.

Deep down, I am glad as hell to be in what seems a paradise of sorts.

First Day

How *good* deep sleep feels is more than I can say. I had imagined I'd be given no pillow, but to find one filled with down is yet another relief.

Having washed my hair and gazed at the view, slightly giddy from sedation, I went to explore the garden and the facilities downstairs. The former is full of mature, huge rose bushes, small benches and – grapes! Do they produce wine? the wrong side of my brain couldn't help wondering.

The ground floor couldn't be more convivial. In addition to what I have already described, there are flowers, paintings on the walls, and even a small room with a coffee or soft drinks automat. I watched people. They all looked rather 'normal', though strikingly indolent. All of a sudden I felt immensely weak myself and went back to my room just as Dottore M was walking into it.

For about an hour he asked apparently innocuous questions, which I answered profusely, as one who has bottled up too many things too long. He took no notes, but observed every detail of my body-language and listened in a way one isn't used to being listened to: with interest and concern. He smiled sometimes, since I can describe embarrassing things with wry humour. I am not a melodramatic person.

At 11.30 on the dot, lunch is brought to the room.

From what I understood, mornings are dedicated to therapy, or to being left in peace, and afternoons to 'activities'.

Today: *art-atelier*. There, you are given the choice between beading collars, painting, building some object with dice-shaped wooden pieces, shikado, assembling a mosaic – whatever. I opted for the mosaic. Lacking geometrical inspiration, I placed small glass pieces of varying shapes and colours to form the letters TQ (*Te quiero*, i.e. 'I love you' in Spanish) on the round cork support.

Next to me sat a good-looking guy in his early forties. We started an easy conversation during which we both exposed our problems. Marco speaks some Spanish, so must have guessed what the capital letters stood for. He remarked mischievously: 'You should add an L. Tequila tastes much better with lemon!' Not only is he handsome and clever, but he has come a long way: a born manic-depressive, he became prey to delusions, the most recent being that he was God's illegitimate son. Medium funny. His three-year-old daughter already has unpredictable frantic fits, and it scares him. His Neapolitan mother was apparently nuts for as long as he can remember. She spent most of her life lying around behind half-drawn curtains.

The afternoon had a surprise in store. *Fiable* means fable or tale in Italian. In the *Gruppo Fiable* gatherings a rather young male nurse called Gianni (or is he a psychologist?) reads a text aloud, and those who have chosen to participate comment on the story, expressing their interpretation, thoughts and feelings. Six of us sat in a circle this afternoon. No: seven, actually, but the sweet 'Music Monk' just puffed on his pipe absent-mindedly.

There is a small kingdom surrounded by big kingdoms. The king is magnanimous and brave – but desperate: not only has he recently lost his cherished wife, but his neighbours are making threatening noises. His only comfort is his lovely, seventeen-year-old daughter, who, apart from being a graceful beauty, has the kindest heart and even temper. *Raison d'état oblige*, he marries a neighbouring queen, also a widow, a dominating and egocentric woman. She brings a daughter of her own into the marriage, the opposite of the lovely princess: ugly, foul tempered and mean. The inevitable tensions rise to a pitch. One day, the lovely princess, in tears, comes to her father and asks: 'Father, please let me go away for a while, and seek my luck in our beloved country, I'm too miserable in this castle.' The king listens, thinks, deliberates and finally grants his daughter's request with a bleeding heart. A basket is prepared for her, containing food and jewellery. They part with much pain and weeping.

She walks and walks and walks in the thick forest, it gets cold and dark, when suddenly she finds herself in a glade. There is a hut and the flickering of a fire next to it. As she approaches, she sees an old man with an abundant white beard. He begs her for something to eat. Being kind, she immediately opens her basket. They share the food in silence. Next morning, rested and warmed up, she bids the old man farewell. He gives her a stick and warns her, 'The bushes are thorny and the paths full of holes, so my child, take this small token of my gratitude. It will help guide you.' She walks and walks and walks, and suddenly stands in front of a pond. Three heads emerge from the water. The redhead implores: 'Please! Wash my hair; I have no arms, and then it can dry in the sun!' The lovely princess accedes without hesitation. As soon as she has done so, the blonde-haired one asks her the same, and when the dark-haired head, also washed and combed, lies peacefully in the sun, cascades of pearls pour out of the three mouths and perfume streams over her. 'Thank you, child,' they smile. The three pairs of eyes, green, blue and hazel, turn to the same direction. 'Go that way, it's very beautiful.' The lovely princess walks and walks and walks until she reaches a valley. Men are hunting, so she hides behind a tree, a little afraid and shy. One of the riders, galloping close by, abruptly turns around, seeking the provenance of such wondrous scent. Upon seeing the princess, the man is thunderstruck by her grace, demeanour and beauty. Softly he lifts her on to his horse and brings her to a castle. It is his castle – for he is a prince. They fall in love and he asks her to marry him. She is overjoyed, but eager to share her happiness with her father. The prince sends a messenger, arrangements are made and on a glorious summer day, they are wedded. Her stepmother and sister-in-law are livid with jealousy and spite; her father is elated, although he must part once more from his beloved daughter.

As soon as the ugly, foul-tempered, mean princess is back home, she starts harassing her mother: 'Mother, I want to go away and seek my luck in the world, I'm too miserable in this country.' The queen listens, flies into a tantrum, hurls imprecations, but finally grants her daughter's request with a boiling heart. A second basket is prepared for her, containing food and jewellery. They part frostily. She walks and walks and walks in the thick forest, it gets cold and dark, when she suddenly finds herself in a glade. There is a hut and a flickering fire next to it.

As she approaches, she sees an old man with an abundant white beard. He begs her for something to eat. Being mean, she immediately hides her basket. Next morning, the good old man gives her a stick to help her on her way. She walks and walks and walks, and suddenly hears three voices: 'Please! Wash my hair; I have no arms, and then it can dry it in the sun!' The ugly princess refuses with disdain and walks on, bothered by the pestilential smell she begins to feel all around her. Wherever she goes, people draw back and flee, or stare and curse. It will always be thus, because this princess isn't only ugly and smelly, she is also foul tempered and mean.

Gianni had read all this in a deep, pleasant voice, with many intonations.

– Well, who'd like to say something?

None of us wanted to speak first.

– What is the tale all about?

– Justice, I ventured. Who gives much is given more in return.

About fatherly love, giving priority to a child's happiness over his own . . .

– . . . and wisdom, said Tonia. Her father lets her go notwithstanding his sorrow, but the bearded man, old and lonely, gives a stick to both the kind and the mean. He is a symbol too . . .

Her voice trailed off, and her eyes became veiled. Marco picked up her sentence:

– . . . of God. He loves all living beings, and will indiscriminately hand over his stick, meaning protection and help, to all. He has hitherto remained silent, as deities should and humans can't.

– What annoys me, interrupted an elderly lady with fantastic hair, is that it is always the ugly who are mean and the beautiful that are kind in that sort of story. Reality is not like that.

– It's a tale, whispered a frail young girl, sitting on the floor near Tonia and looking up at her for assent. It doesn't need to reflect reality, but to give hope and examples . . . nice people are happier, I think, regardless of how they look.

– Here, the mother only allows her daughter to go her own way with the ambitious hope she might profit from it, in sharp contrast to the father. Why are mothers always shown as jealous, embittered creatures? launched a woman my age, rather severe looking, who, as I learnt later, was called Rose and had four children, one of whom had run away and hadn't been seen since.

– Not always, corrected the reader-psychologist.

He gave several examples of tales in which, on the contrary, mothers are 'good' and fathers 'bad'. But Rose's irritation did not subside:

– Also, it's always the *men* who choose and decide in that *fairy* world of tales . . . What kind of fairness is that?

– Things have changed, Marco remarked sardonically.

– I think it was safer before, said the young girl, because men know better. Women are weak, and children cruel. Fifteen seconds of pleasure for twenty years' aggravation, that's what childbearing means.

Rose looked at her with haughty compassion, but didn't press it. The rest of us were stunned by the cynicism of such a statement coming from such a young thing.

– Morality? asked Gianni.

– Many travel the same path in life, but the outcome of each one's journey depends on how you behave, at which stages you stop, said Tonia pensively, and how well equipped you are against danger. You're on your own.

– Wisdom is bountiful when you have reaped the right fruits at the right moment, said the elderly lady, Reni. When you are young, it's guts you need, more than intelligence or experience.

– I agree with Tonia and with Reni, I said with sudden passion. Experience is a lantern one carries on one's back. It only illuminates the already trodden track. Besides, as a French saying goes, *Le bonheur de malheurs évités se compose*, meaning that happiness is composed of avoided misery, accidents for instance . . .

Tonia looked at me with surprise.

– I think the whole thing is an ad for L'Oréal, interjected Marco. 'Perfume yourself, you'll be worth it!'

His faked candour made us all laugh. The session went on for longer, but all right . . . First reactions are give-aways.

As we were leaving the big salon, a strange boy, flanked by a Rambo-type male nurse, walked in. He didn't look strange, actually: he looked like the average teenager of about sixteen, with the inevitable baseball cap and logo-stamped T-shirt, but there was something sneaky about him . . . the feline gait perhaps? I went to get a coffee and before ascending the stairs heard a familiar cartoon soundtrack. Yes, I recognized it from *The Jungle Book*. What a nice pastime, I thought, but quite incongruous with the bullish surveillance. I was too tired to wonder any further and headed for a nap.

As I returned to my room, some lady doctor appeared with a psychological test consisting of . . . 533 questions. She said I had until Monday to fill it out (only yes or no answers), but once started, I felt the urge to complete it. With the help of some 'victims' to translate the words I didn't understand, I finished just in time for the nine o'clock infusion. I am intrigued to learn about the meaning of it all. I have lied only once.

Whatever they pump into you, it works. I fell asleep minutes after the nurse had stuck the needle into a vein.

First Weekend

I received the results of Thursday's blood test. No anomaly; even the liver is in pristine form. I'm slightly amused, frankly. Much too high cholesterol though. I've known that for years, but keep forgetting to take the prescribed pills. What I didn't know is that alcohol has a lot to do with it.

Saturday afternoons, games are proposed. Today, it was the Italian variation on 'Trivial Pursuit'. You can choose a speciality. I turned to Marco and suggested theology. He grinned. I took literature and fared badly.

Communication is piecemeal. Some people ostentatiously cringe away from it; others are glad to talk. In any case, it is neither encouraged nor discouraged. But already after two days I have learnt a little about several people.

Tonia, the one who suffered a relapse into coke and heroine addiction after ten years of abstinence, panicked the night she found herself asleep on the loo with a broken tooth. Dottore M immediately agreed to her coming to the clinic, on condition she would be in the closed section. She seems so healthy and extrovert, so highly intelligent and dynamic and strong as a well-structured rock, that it is difficult to imagine her in sordid situations. She has just extended her stay (already three weeks) for another week, terrified of going back to Milan and temptation.

Here for two months so far, still quite a zombie and following Tonia everywhere, is the pretty young girl who had joined the *Gruppo Fiabe*. Kiki's angelic smile is spooky. She spent half a year in a community which turned out to be a fiendish sect, was brainwashed to the point of losing her marbles, her brother's

34

money and her free will. They totally and utterly drugged her with psychotropic substances, LSD or derivatives. Her memory is damaged, and so is her lymphatic system. She explained it all as if talking about another person.

Raff, who sits for hours on the balcony next to mine and keeps to himself, told me of his drinking problem: three bottles of rosé a day . . . one more than my average dose, but similar in pattern. A few glasses in the morning; none at noon because of business lunches; but later on, knocking back the stuff as if there were no tomorrow. A few months ago, he drove somewhere with his teenaged daughter, pretty plastered but not stone drunk. He caused an accident that injured her seriously. That did it. I believe he may well never touch alcohol again in his life. He is destroyed, even though the daughter has recovered fully. Remorse nags at his every nerve. He seldom smiles.

I asked him if he knew the silent man I call the 'Music Monk'. He shrugged.

– All I know is that he has been here for a year or so, behaves like he wants to be treated like a child again. Guess life has been tough ever since he left his village, somewhere in the heart of Sicily . . .

– Oh? Where in Sicily?

– Bronte, apparently a remote and forsaken place. Giuseppe was chased from the village when his parents died. They thought of him as a fool or a devil, can't remember and can't imagine why, he's a really nice fellow.

Raff hid behind his newspaper, indicating the interview was over.

Bronte . . . I had wanted to visit the village, perhaps a small town by now, last time I crossed the island, but bad weather prevented me. I thought it would be interesting to see the lands given to Nelson by the king of Naples as a token of gratitude for the admiral's help in halting Napoleon's conquest of the island. (I had also met the last Duke of Bronte.) More interesting was its history. Small Bronte had been the bone of contention for some big power struggles, not only once but twice. The peasant up-heaval unleashed by Garibaldi's opportunistic promise, in 1860, when he needed to rally the Sicilian population to the cause of the Savoys, to hand over the land they worked to the peasants, caused ravages to agriculture and vindictive killings of all hat-wearers (the *galantuomi*, or gentlemen), as opposed to those who wore berets or caps. However, as this particular enclave belonged to Nelson's lineage, and as Cavour coveted an alliance with the British as well as with the influential gentry in order to unify Italy, a bloody repression was waged, resulting in the slaughter of hundreds, perhaps thousands of peasants.

One detail had been particularly stressed in the account of I forgot which chronicler: the dwarf and the village fool were shot. This is given much importance, for while in those days the disposal of dwarfs, considered malefic beings, was of no note-worthy consequence, the killing of a fool was tantamount to sacrilege: a court jester or a village fool was endowed, in those superstitions, with divine attributes, or even origins. Dementia was regarded as a holy trait.

Disregarding chronology, I imagined Giuseppe, the 'Music Monk', in that context, and felt very sad again.

Was this clinic as a monastery to him?

Sunday, 3 June

The church bells were ringing, the sky didn't cry.

Day off. No programme, apart from a brief visit by some psycho-or-other who seemed distracted. I might look like a Caesar sculpture inside, but outside, I begin to resemble a fakir, with prick marks all over my arms from all the needles they've had stuck into them. After a long bubble bath, I wanted to go jogging round the garden. No way. In spite of ten hours' sleep and a panoply of vitamins, I feel as weak as it can get.

So I sat on the downstairs veranda with a book I had bought before coming by an author called Tierno, *A Complete Manual of*

Positive Psychology. Complete? Whatever: being rather literary, it turned out to be a pleasant read.

In short, it is about self-control, and the attitude required not to be poisoned by one's own pessimism – when not doomed to be blatantly pathogenic and destructive. The author reiterates time and again that reality changes the way we can decide to change ourselves. The puzzle of personality can be mustered. Balance is an apprenticeship. 'There is a big difference between fighting against death and fighting for life: between fighting to save life and fighting to remain alive' (Malaparte). Hmm. Who was finally going to provide the operating and maintenance instructions?

Tierno also warns about too much prudence in life, of the kind that impairs your progress in moving forwards and towards others. He cites Jorge Luis Borges, my philosophical guru at some point (with Ortega y Gasset). What follows is tinged with sarcasm.

> I belong to those people who never go anywhere without a thermometer, a hot-water bottle, an umbrella and a parachute. Should I live again, I would travel more lightly.

- I would intend to commit more mistakes.
- I would try not to be so perfect.
- I would relax more.
- I would be more stupid than I am.
- I would take very few things seriously.
- I would be less obsessed with hygiene.
- I'd take more risks.
- I would watch more sunsets.
- I would climb more mountains.
- I would swim in more rivers.
- I would explore more places.
- I would eat more ice-cream and less beans.
- I would have more real problems and fewer imaginary ones.

According to Tierno, Borges realized that to dedicate oneself to the sheer enjoyment of *available* realities would make life so much simpler and better.

In my opinion, Borges was pulling the reader's leg. He was very pleased with himself, quite misogynous, and spent his last years in not exactly exotic Geneva. I know he was blind, I know he was a loner; possibly, he was depressed too, to which that city can act as an efficient placebo – when not causing the disease.

There is another story about Borges, a true one, which I find quite extraordinary.

As his eyesight dwindled, he employed a young girl to read for him. He loved travel books, and of course, the young girl of modest origins became increasingly fascinated by descriptions of far-away places. She was also sweet; he became fond of her. After many months of secret correspondence, he announced: 'I want to thank you. As a gift, I have arranged for you to spend two months in Europe with friends of mine, all expenses paid.' She gaped. Then she remained silent for a long while. Finally she said: 'I am very touched, but no thank you, I don't want to go.' 'What?' boomed Borges, in utter disbelief. 'No,' she repeated softly but trenchantly.

He often related this anecdote, concluding with a thunderous: '*This* is freedom.'

Back to the book (subtitled 'You are the Architect of Your Life'): a passage made quite an impact on me:

Psychologists know first-hand the decisive importance of references for a child, given that at the beginning, most of what he does is by imitation, and that examples give impulses (*exempla trahunt*); hence the optimism or the pessimism of parents contaminates the child and transfers itself, on the mode of communicating vases, unto him. I ascertained that a child is so vulnerable to the state of mind of his parents that not only during youth and adolescence, but also in adulthood, mother or father remain the dominating emotional influence. [Now comes the staggering bit.] Curiously, it is the more negative, whining, insecure and hurtful influence – not only mothers, as one tends to think – which imposes itself . . . Fortunately, this is not irreversible. This mechanism can be corrected if, at the right time, a strong, vigorous, confident and positive person appears, with whom a constant and trusting relationship develops.

In early life these were, among others, Johannot and Morales at boarding school (the headmaster and the Spanish teacher); perhaps more significantly still, my maverick, free-spirited friend Archie in London, where I could easily have sunk into alluring but treacherous quicksands; and later, the flamboyant publisher I worked for, also a mentor and a friend.

The affirmation regarding the pre-eminence of the negative person in the parent-couple made me pensive. If there was a dissuasive example to me, it was my mother. Far from wanting to resemble her, I wished to be her exact opposite. This, however, is a reaction that demands much hostile feeling and presupposes a constant watchfulness. Could this be more determinant than imitating and approving – as with my father?

Another striking passage: according to the Psychiatric Institute of the NYU, women are twice as exposed to depression as men, essentially from hormonal factors and fluctuations. As to the WHO (World Health Organization), depression will, by 2020, be the predominant cause of invalidity or disability, physical and mental. They end their report with a laconic 'depression is the plague of the twenty-first century'. It being a disease that spreads faster in rich countries, it leads to pointed questions: are we doomed to want forever more, must everything get bigger and better, smarter and faster? Have we unlearnt the faculty to recognize privilege and satiation? Should a kind of civil service be introduced, requiring the privileged to spend three weeks a year in Siberia or Ghana?

Most patients in this clinic – at least in this section – seem to suffer from depression, but of course, for reasons and causes as manifold as perceptions are subjective.

The refrain of a song I once wrote crossed my mind:

> When I'm sulking
> I'm silently begging
> for something vital I'm ready
> to refuse if you get near
> or to scream if you don't hear

I wandered around the garden, in circles. It isn't very big, and I missed exercising. The feline teenager was sneaking about, not going anywhere either. He intrigued me. There was something extremely disagreeable about the character, but I could not pinpoint what. When I saw him sitting down on the grass, I strolled towards him and asked if he would mind my sitting with him. To my amazement, he smiled broadly and even stood up, holding out a hand.

– Sure, he said, visibly glad.

– You're the only English person I met here so far, I smiled.

– American, he corrected, exaggerating the accent.

– That's a fair way from home . . . How come you are here?

– My mother is Italian. She lives in Parma.

– Really? I live in Palma, in Spain.

– Cool. What the fuck are *you* doing here?

– Trying to get my act together, stop drinking, get some sleep, think, basically.

– Cool.

– Why didn't you join in at the *atelier*? It's fun.

– I don't know a fucking soul, he retorted, don't want to either.

– Why not?

– Want to get out.

– You only just arrived!

– Yeah. Same day as you. I saw you and thought to myself, at least one pretty sight around.

– Thanks. But it isn't too bad, is it? Give the place a chance, you might even . . .

– Don't bother.

A leaden silence followed.

– What's your name? I asked, retreating on to neutral ground.

– Rick. And yours?

– Aleana.

– Weird one.

– I know. I was named after a boat.

– Megacool. Do you act like a boat?

– Don't think so, I smiled, but I guess being driven by random winds as I have been lately, I need a new compass. And you? Why are you in this clinic?

– Long story. Not pretty.

He grinned, then laughed.

– You're a cool cat, I said, with a twinkle in the eye, using, I hoped, one of his favourite expressions.

I must have done something very wrong. He sprang to his feet as if bitten by a tarantula, fired me a fierce glance, aghast and alarmed, spitting more than saying:

– Curiosity kills cats!

He ran away, as if chased by demons. That guy was weird after all. It only increased my sadness, which, I mused, came from the feeling that people allowed you to get close only so long as you did not infringe. On what, exactly? What is closeness if you have to block a door with your foot or mind, instead of waving it ajar, ever so softly?

My thoughts returned to the book I had been perusing a while back, and the decisive role played by spiritual door-openers such as Archie or my boss and friend the publisher. Then as now, I had determined not to sink into facileness, and then as now, I had needed help. London in the eighties was the land of missed opportunities, largely due to self-complacency. My friends were twenty or thirty something and, unlike my fellow students, fast learners of the 'inheritance business'. With them I shrugged off my attending the LSE as some casual toying around to avoid being called an intellectual (not a compliment) while they footled about in the relentless pursuit of pleasure. 'One does the best one can – as little as one can,' they joked. There were exceptions, of course. Yet by and large I led a double life: on the one hand, studying, or later on working, representing steadiness and sanity; on the other, thoroughly enjoying the company of the carefree, frivolous no-gooders, hanging on in nightclubs or party-hopping in helicopters. Most of the people I am thinking of were kind, generous, smart and loads of fun. There was a lot of booze and drug consumption among the idle. That's why I referred to the social scene, back then, as quicksands for someone such as me.

I needed protection against myself, for as Oscar Wilde remarked, it is easy to resist everything except temptation. I might well never have completed my studies, nor sought recognition of a sort more important than appearance, had it not been for Archie.

Archie was a knight in a silver white tie, with the armour of revenge. He had been rather frail as a boy, and treated accordingly by the inevitable bullies of the British schooling system. Having won a daunting race, he discovered how the pernicious morality of 'The Tortoise and the Hare' myth could be turned to his advantage. Lacking muscle, he developed wings – not of the giant sort which prevent a man from walking, but wings to deploy a scope wide enough for a man to be larger than life, and to forge his entrepreneurial legend.

Women, I think, scared him. I was a hybrid something, some-where in between a larva and a butterfly, neither mutating too fast nor flying too high. In other words, I was no threat. I was an assiduous reader, happy when left in peace – as was he. We made an easy-going team. He provided the pace; I followed the rhythm, eager not to miss a beat. A loner scrutinized by the public eye, Archie was as much exposed to snide criticism as to encomium.

As with all determinant influences in one's life, it was by virtue of giving an example, not delivering diatribes, that he protected me. I shall never forget his reading *Journey to Java* by Harold

Nicolson to me, and I still wish a flying carpet could transport us to that country, in space and time.

As for Najar, the publisher, he was during two years a daily vitamin injection. Never since have I come across someone with such mind-blowing energy, vitality and resilience. A bulldozer he was too, ruthless in his progress towards achievement and fame. He injected a fossilized, nepotism-infected literary scene with new blood, be it of blue, green or red origin. Both boastful and modest, flashy out of insecurity, choleric but mainly for the show value, this bombastic character gave life a five-dimensional proportion far removed from the small talk I joined in at night about the comparative merits of Gstaad *v.* St Moritz, Jonquerts *v.* Pershings, this or that restaurant, and other such matters of cardinal relevance.

Both mentors shared a passion for 'drilling and exploring', Archie for ideals and profit, Najar for ideas and risk. They also had in common a peculiar gentleness behind brash façades. Both were overpowering in certain ways, huggable in others. Both gave me faith in myself when I most needed it.

What happened since, to make me feel so 'small' again? A lot.

Monday

At the *atelier*, my mosaic looked better than I had expected.

Dottoressa D came for a long talk, again about childhood and parents, but also about Robin and our marriage.

I only have lovely things to say about him, how joyous and tender he is and how good to me and for me; how absolute our mutual trust is, and how we have, while sharing the same weaknesses, complementary skills and strengths. He is disorganized and disciplined; I'm the reverse. He is scientific and factual; I'm literary and a fantasist. We share the same sense of humour and taste.

– This sounds wonderful, she says amiably, but why don't you live together? Don't you suffer from these endless separations, from a lack of roots?

There, of course, she struck a sensitive nerve.

As far as roots are concerned, I never really had any. I was brought up in Paris and Switzerland; studied in London and Madrid; lived between Geneva and Paris for twelve years, now in Spain for almost ten. My parents moved flats five times while I was a child, and my count of how many times I moved is muddled. I don't suffer from rootlessness. It's a way of life like any other and, on the conscious level at least, not a traumatic one.

– You married in your mid forties, from what I understand?

I nodded, expecting her to ask: 'Why so late?' She did.

– I have been asked that before, as you may imagine, I smiled, which annoyed her a little. I never answer with the typical, 'Because the right man hadn't crossed my path.' Two or three men did cross my sentimental trajectory, and there I must indulge the 'wrong time, wrong place' cliché. Two men really counted before Robin. The first might have been the right one. I was too young to

44

anticipate possible regret: I was a student, Lars was divorcing; he would wake up when I came back from university, and mix with the show-biz crowd in which I hardly fitted. More determinant was that he travelled light years ahead of me in terms of emotional imagination and intelligence. His is one third Greek, one third Norwegian, one third American, but like all men who attracted me, Latin at heart. I was ruthless, not for wanting to end our relationship, but because of the brutal way I did it. Now that I know better I much regret it. The second man who counted was Hugo, the man who drove me to the clinic the other day, and to whom I am still devoted. He had been separated for twenty-odd years when we met in the early 1990s, but was trapped in a financial arrangement that transformed a possible divorce into a highjacking with war as a bonus. I only found out by coincidence. Two days later, a miscarriage . . . I had been pregnant, and happy.

I tried to sound offhand, but burst into silent tears, the kind that choke off sobs. Again, I couldn't stop.

The *dottoressa* waited, also in silence. I was grateful to her for that. After about ten minutes, she asked:

– Is Robin the right man?

– Yes.

My puffed eyes must have lightened up, for she felt she could continue:

– What was it about him that convinced you he was?

– Oh God! How do you explain – not within a split second, but within less than an hour, more unconsciously than not – why you feel profoundly at ease with someone, so much so that you *know* you are likely to feel *at peace* with that someone? Hasn't this enigma been written about in prose and poetry, in languages dead and alive?

She did not smile, expecting straight answers not circum-volutions; and waited.

– Look, *dottoressa*, I continued, the feeling of love is less complicated than its tiresome dissection, usually post mortem. Once in a while, if you are lucky – and receptive – you sit in front of a person whom you like globally, all at once. I met Robin at a cocktail party given by my parents, not really the most titillating setting, but okay. We talked in Spanish, which created a first complicity in the midst of a German-speaking assembly, but . . . there was so much more only eyes could tell. What do you take in, and in what order, on the spur of a lasting moment? The whole picture, I would say. A nasal voice, coarse hands or a glassy glance can sweep away any remote chance of further attention, but when all you see is *warm*, and so is the voice, well, your attention is hooked and your heart, when not saturated with love for another, stands ajar. My cousin, who had brought him to the party, told me that Robin was immune to relationships, still in mourning after a nasty divorce. He had described me as a glamorous playgirl flying only first-class. My cousin being none too subtle, he meant aeroplanes.

This made me laugh.

– He was wrong about Robin too. After a year of misery indeed, he had embarked on a round of womanizing, be it to catch up or to reassure himself. When we met, he had achieved both. I had recently emerged from a casual affair with a Peter O'Toole clone, devastating charm and alcoholism included. Was ours a happy 'timing'? Would Robin never have sought a second encounter had the first taken place years, months or days earlier – or later than on this occasion? We will never know.

Having relegated speculations about the past to one of my (b)locked drawers, I had no intention of rummaging in it. Not so Dottoresa D.

– Will you not continue your anxious search for . . . the novelty and exhilaration that seems part of your imbalance?

– No. Not in the sentimental realm. Robin is part of me. Do you know what he said the second, only the second time we met? He said: 'I sense *our perspective.*' I didn't immediately understand the scope of his words. Now I do. He recognized me before I recognized him. I was scared of long-distance relationships, I'd had enough of those, and then my cousin's words resounded as a warning in my mind, but it all took a natural course, without haste or tremors. Robin is the best person that ever happened in my entire life. He represents an anchor and a boat, stability and movement. He is deeply *good*, and fun too. I'm damn lucky.

– Sorry to repeat myself, but wouldn't you rather live together, the way married couples normally do?

– If we were normal, would I be here? I grinned.

She raised a severe eyebrow.

– All right, all right: seriously speaking, our present arrangement, however peculiar, is temporary and not without its redeeming aspects: we are both sociable loners and manage to spend a third of each month together.

– Are you not worried about temptations that *he* might succumb to, seductive and charming as you describe him?

– No. I am as jealous as any woman can be, but not suspicious. I have total faith in his faithfulness. At our age, and he is seven years older, we are only too aware of the fragility of luck. Neither of us would risk putting it into peril for a caprice.

– Not even you?

The woman, it seemed, distrusted my sincerity. It may have been her job, but I resented it and riposted with vehemence:

– No, *dottoressa*. Even less than him, possibly.

> I have seen flowers come in stony places
> And kind things done by men with ugly faces,
> And the gold cup won by the worst horse at the races,
> > So I trust, too.

In myself not least, and at last, if you help me . . .

– Moving poem.

– Better known than Masefield and also to the point is Byron's famous

> Day and night my toils redouble
> Never nearer to the goal.
> Night and day I feel the trouble
> Of the wanderer in my soul.

47

Does that describe you?

It pretty much describes my past, even though I always believed that the man one loves replaces roots, representing them *per se*. Marrying Robin has made me feel, if not having reached the goal, that the goal may be striven for and reachable together.

I am no longer alone! Had I not been afraid of sounding silly, I would have cried it aloud with puerile hope.

– How would you define that goal?

– As the feeling of belonging. For better and for worse. Forever.

– I see. Tell me about 'the perspective' in practical terms.

I reflected, but not for long.

– The part that does in truth worry me is that I have no precise idea what the future will be like. Sometimes Robin says he will be able to stop working in two years, but I know Robin's adoration for his children. His ex-wife will continue pressurizing him, using them. I also know the woman; she is no lady.

– You're telling me when it comes to ex's, the *dottoressa* sighed. I've had to deal with two. But please go on about the perspective, Aleana.

– I have a clear idea of what I would like us to do later on: own and run a small but elegant *agroturismo*, that kind of *hôtel de charme* where your guests are mostly friends and friends of friends. Robin remains vague. I doubt the idea thrills him as much as it thrills me. He doesn't seem decided as to whether he prefers Spain or Italy (having been raised in the former but being of Italian origin). Nor do I, loving both countries. His thoughts haven't reached that far as yet. My main concern is to have a proximity to the Mediterranean, since I am a passionate swimmer and sea-lover in general. Robin is not passionate. He is sentimental and romantic, but passionate? No.

– In other words, it's all hazy and vague? No deadlines, no destination?

– One could put it that way.

– You must, I'm afraid. This situation accounts in no small measure for your anxieties, as you are probably aware.

Venice came into my mind; with it a sense of unease.

The first trip we ever made together, six years before, was to some place near Venice. I had to return to Majorca. Robin took me to the airport. We were last in the queue, and as I was looking for something in my handbag, a breathless man appeared before us.

When I handed ticket and passport over the counter I was told in a desolate voice that the flight had been overbooked (typically Alitalia) and that alas, pardon, so sorry, I could not board it, the last seat having been allocated to the man who should have been standing behind me if he'd kept his place in the queue. Robin never raised his voice, made no scandal, but merely asked the employee what other arrangements could be made. I couldn't believe it. This was a blatant injustice, and he knew it, yet he neither argued nor banged his fist on the counter. It then took me forty-eight hours to get to Palma, via Milan, with one night in Madrid, plus hours waiting in Barcelona, before finally getting home. But that was not the issue.

The issue is that I should have realized there and then that Robin is no fighter. He is not assertive. Not jumping queues yourself doesn't justify letting others get away with it. Good manners have their limits, frankly, and never imposing an opinion or a rule is borderline . . . something.

When he discovered his ex-wife had an affair, what did he do? Nothing. When she packed his bags, where did he go? To his own guest room. And when she filed for a divorce? He gave in. To be separated from his daughters was agony. Where they are concerned he's a teddy bear. They have intuitively understood how to lead him by both nose and heart, obtaining everything when hinting, on suitable occasions, that their mother – whose intelligence and excellent education were never in doubt, incidentally – wouldn't let them do this or buy that.

I expressed none of these thoughts and reminiscences to Dottoressa D. Not with any intention to conceal, but because to do so would have seemed grossly unfair and ungrateful. Robin is always on my side, at my side, if not geographically, then effectively. Like most men, he is an adamant no-conflict person, and being bright, he ultimately achieves what he strives for.

Above all, he is an ally, a friend, a lover, and my husband.

What I did tell her is how lucky I am that his kids adore me, and likewise I them. Not only have I married a man I love, but I now feel part of a small family. He gets his endearing qualities from his mother. I also told her my regret that he never talks about what bothers or preoccupies him. His upbringing accounts for that, I sighed: one keeps one's problems to oneself. Never complain, never explain, etcetera. Nor does he talk about his work, which represents a whole third of his time and life. Regrettably it does create a gap.

– What about children? she asked cautiously. Aren't you sad not to have any of your own?

That particular question struck no sensitive nerve, shocking as it may sound.

– You know, I did want to have some of course, but for the wrong reasons: as a way of creating an indissoluble bond with a man. I told you about my pregnancy from Hugo: it wasn't so much motherhood as the alliance I looked forward to. Even at the zenith of our relationship, I was afraid that it might end unless a child cemented it all and prevented us from doing what nowadays is elementary 'first aid': pack and go. I did exactly that, of course. Anyway, I doubt I have the proper instincts. Even as a child, I only played with fluffy animals, never with dolls. Babies scare me. In fact, so do young children. I find their cruel streak terrifying, like their innate gift for manipulation and lies.

To my surprise, the *dottoressa* began to laugh and said:

– A bleak picture indeed, but it has the merit of being clear. Do you believe there can be a substitute for that particular bond?

– I do. Sorry if I bore you with my literary references, but I can't help it: I read so much. There is a short story by Dorothy Parker titled 'Advice to the Little Peyton Girl', which I discovered too late in life to be able to apply it earlier. I remember whole bits of it by heart. Basically, an experienced seductress, Miss Marcon, lectures a young and naïve girl, Sylvie, with a thing or two about men and the handling of relationships. She is not as cynical as Madame de Merteuil in *Les Liaisons Dangereuses*, but is just as clinical. In any event, Miss Marcon is damn right. Men are all the same age, she says, in that they hate and seek the same things: no reproaches, no reminders of sadness or weakness, no straightening out of unpleasantness: they detest talking things over. 'You showed him he was all important to you. Men do not like that. You must be light and you must be easy, for ease is the desire of all men. Nothing so embarrasses a man as to see a woman lose her dignity. You must conquer your fears, dear child. A woman in fear for her love can never do right. Love is a quicksilver in the hand, Sylvie. Leave the fingers open and it stays in the palm; clutch it, and it darts away. Be, above all things, always calm. *Let it be peace to be with you.*' And so on. I paused for effect, feeling perky all of a sudden.

– Morality, dear *dottoressa*: alcohol is the most dangerous of liaisons.

She laughed again:

– I shall buy this enlightening book. It's never too late, is it?

– You tell me.

– It is never too late, given patience and perseverance.

After she left in a good mood, I felt the sudden urge to talk to Robin. I had told him I wouldn't be able to call for a week, unaware there would be a phone booth downstairs for use at any time. For some reason I cannot identify, the urge then vanished.

We have agreed to talk on Thursday. So be it.

Tuesday

5 June

I am re-editing my short story 'Double' so I can give a copy to Dottore M. Even though the circumstantial context is pure fiction, there are facts about my past, about events in nineteen ninety-one and my pulsations back then, which might be relevant to him. I had to correct so many things, shorten so many sentences, alter the structure in so many instances, that I wondered at how idiotic I must have been in presenting the story to publishers in its former version.

Could it be I am a lot more clear-headed now? A specious question, of course.

At noon I was given a massage which relaxed my aching neck and spine. Then came an hour of 'music therapy', an interesting waste of time.

Laid out on a long table were dozens of percussion, string, metal or glass instruments, from Persian lyres, Tibetan cymbals, African doum-doums or kpanlogos to Indian flutes or bendirs, from xylophones or tubular bells to oriental miniature kinds of piano, ocean drums (big boxes containing tiny metal balls which, when slanted and rolled, produce the sound of waves), rain sticks (a tube producing the hissing of wind); and those sand-filled objects you shake for the rhythm. There were only four of us, and after some breathing control and voice practice, we were given no instructions whatsoever except to choose whichever instrument we wished and get on with it.

The 'teacher' participated, but it was clear he was also observing our every move to assess coordination of hands, choice of instruments, spontaneity, etc.

After twenty minutes I was bored stiff. All this noise led no-where, and it all seemed rather absurd. But all right, I had decided to abide by all the rules, so on it went. In the end, our instructor took me aside and suggested that next time I try hitting instruments a little harder. He had noticed I only liked those producing a little ting-a-ling-linging, mostly Asiatic instruments: 'You should assert yourself more.'

What had most intrigued me was the sonic pyramid inside which it was possible to sit to feel the vibrations from the heli-coidally magnetic vortex. But we were not allowed, and none of us regretted it, the whole thing having sounded like hieroglyphs anyway. After the others left, I asked Jacques whether he would allow me to take a photograph of the instruments (cameras being strictly forbidden, for confidentiality reasons). He agreed, but urged me to be quick. Since we were alone, and he seemed more relaxed about the rules than the permanent staff, I asked whether he knew the 'Music Monk', who not surprisingly had not shown up. Jacques smiled:

– I thought you might ask that.

– Why?

– Never mind. He and I have special sessions together, and Aleana, I'm the one who's learning.

– Well . . . he seems able to read staves of music as others read books.

– Not only that. At first, I thought he might be autistic, or else simple-minded. Not so! The man is a genius.

– Really? He looks, you might say, simple . . .

– His mind being too fast for communication, he retreated into silence. He cannot write, for instance, not because he's analpha-betic, but because his fingers move too fast for legibility. Gifted people's writing often cannot keep pace with their thoughts.

I waited for Jacques to continue but did not dare press him. Fortunately, he now seemed oblivious of me and dreamily went on. Perhaps our talking in French helped to infringe upon the secrecy regarding patients that the personnel pledge to respect.

So what? Telling Giuseppe's life-story was no indiscretion. It was extraordinary.

– In the village in north-eastern Sicily where he was born, he was considered a freak, like people who don't fit the mould. A child prodigy can be regarded as retarded in an environment such as rural, backward Bronte. Chronically absent-minded, with corresponding bad grades, he was ridiculed by children his own age – a frequent fate of gifted children. They become bored, hence impatient. Realizing that being short-tempered alienates the very people they want to be accepted by, they often retreat into muteness: not being understood is preferable to being mis-understood. Understanding everything at once, they lapse, on the other hand, into utter disinterest where studies are con-cerned. Spiritual loneliness weighs on their soul. As also often happens, they turn to the Church. Historically, priests have always protected the outcasts, the more so when they perceive them as 'enlightened'. Well. One sad day, Giuseppe's whole family burns to death when their farm catches fire. All of a sudden, his former school companions let fly with all the aggression that his aloof behaviour and his preferential treatment from the community's father figure, i.e. the priest, have generated over the years. Giuseppe, barely eighteen, flees his home town and heads for the port of Messina. Somewhere along the road there stands a steaming car. A pipe-smoking, dishevelled man waves to him, hoping for help. The young boy's knowledge of engines is nil; other than donkey carts and tractors, he has hardly seen a moving vehicle. Yet, observing the mechanism, Giuseppe deduces how it functions. He even manages to repair it. His previous ignorance has not gone unnoticed by the meditative man, who is none other than Alessandro Faedo, a mathematician who introduced infor-matics as a science at Pisa's university in 1969.

Jacques looked at me as if he himself had been driving and was surprised to discover he'd picked up a hitchhiker. Afraid he might draw back, I smiled timidly, and he continued:

– You may guess what happens next. The professor takes the boy under his wing. A few years later, Giuseppe is working with him on the Sirio satellite project, the first of the short-wave kind used in telecommunications, financed by the CNR. But he becomes bored again, starts inventing computer programs, and then computer games. He makes a fortune but does not know what to spend it on. A pretty assistant of his does. She seduces him, he marries her, and gone with the wind are both the girl and the money.

I thought of the epigraph my cousin Christina had chosen for a book on this very theme, which described the gifted person's hypersensitivity and said something like, 'To him, a touch is a blow, a sound a noise, a misfortune a tragedy, a joy ecstasy, a friend a lover, a lover god. Failure is death.'

– Apart from anything else, his games were no longer commercial, since only very, very few could figure out how to win, always supposing they could work out how to play them at all.

Jacques paused, before sighing deeply:

– Giuseppe wanted to die. Being a good Catholic, the only way to achieve this was to starve to death. He was found about a year ago, a sober tramp among drunken wrecks, on the shore of the Arno. They discovered Alessandro Faedo's telephone number in his pocket, but he had died six years before. His son sent him here.

– Does Giuseppe talk to you?

– No. You are bound to ask how I know all this.

– . . .

– Don't ask me why I trust you. Here is *my* confession: I felt so strongly for that guy, I so intensely wished I could help him overcome his chagrin – he still dreams about that wife of his, probably because before her he never felt the caresses or the warm softness of a woman's skin . . . where was I, yes, well, let's say I 'borrowed' his file from the clinic's secretariat. My version is, naturally, a bit embellished, but a story can't have relief or melody, can it, without adding a moustache here or a storm there?

We both laughed sadly, and for a fraction of a second I visualized being a bowed instrument in his long fine hands. Wrong place, wrong time.

– Jacques. One last question please: what did you learn from him?

– Too long to tell right now. See you next week?

I grimaced. He chuckled.

– Till next week then.

Still under the spell of the moving narrative, I was intercepted on my way to the garden and ushered into a room where two men in white submitted me to a Rorschach test. One of them spoke Spanish, which helped tremendously, because not only was I presented with two dozen of those weird pictures to elicit a spontaneous reaction, but I was then asked to explain my interpretation of each and every one. I rather enjoyed it, and of course was curious about any results or conclusions.

At the end they asked how I felt. I beamed.

– Wonderful! they beamed back.

I also told them what I profoundly believe: that anti-depressants and other medication would certainly not have had the same effect unless complemented by my renewed (it had been atrophied for months that seemed years) passion to write and ability to do it.

– Wonderful, they said again.

All these doctors, one nicer than the next, irritated me to the raw: friendly but impassive faces, and no valuable feedback.

The sun had come out by then, so I sat on the veranda with my ever dearer 'friend' Tonia, who is inseparable from the handsome Marco, formerly God's secret offspring. We smoked and chatted. (Most patients smoke a lot here, for understandable reasons.) Now comes a scoop: as I asked Tonia about her profession, she answered just as casually:

– I'm a psychiatrist.

The cigarette dropped out of my hand.

Sure enough, Kiki, who fell into the trap of a monstrous sect and is the one of the two persons here who really *look* a bit loony, surfaced. She constantly makes you feel like hugging her. She seems desperately disorientated. Her legs were bruised: I asked if she had fallen down. She pulled up her sleeves: both her arms were furrowed with parallel cuts and scars. I had heard of self-mutilation, but never realized the sheer horror of it.

As it started getting cold, we moved to the smoking salon, where you can play cards and other games, or read the daily newspapers. Unfortunately, the radio is monopolized by the second 'loony' I have come across so far. She is a fat blonde suffering from chronic mania: she can't sit still, turns up the music full volume non-stop, changes the station every five minutes and her outfits five times a day, starts dancing in a compulsive manner, chain smokes and is, on top of a being a nuisance, very rude. Why no one interferes, I have no clue. Levels of tolerance in this clinic are stunning. When she walks in, everybody leaps out.

I went to my room and leafed through a book I had included in my packing. I realize I describe too many lectures, but what else am I to do in my spare time? Words on paper really do, somehow, match the mind's monologues. Be that as it may, this is what I came across:

> We should return to the old truth stating that only he who is prepared to be subordinate, to show abnegation and gradually submit to discipline, progresses on the path to self-knowledge and freedom. Only surmounted difficulties allow happiness to be experienced as a rewarding deliverance . . . Are not many tears required before playing the violin or the piano comes to provide pride and joy?

Striking words in this day and age of permissiveness, where the cult of self-gratification discredits authoritarian precepts.

The lines were written not by Caesar or Clausewitz, but by the headmaster of one of Germany's most prestigious private boarding schools, Schloss Salem. Founded in 1920, it was considered from the start to be pretty liberal (both sexes were admitted, new pedagogic methods experimented with). Until recently, and for thirty-one years, it was directed by the author of this book, awarded the Cross of Merit. *In Praise of Discipline* unleashed a storm of controversy with its suggestions that small children needed to be removed from the influences of their overprotective mothers, because only by being submitted to communal laws would they experience justice and learn the need to share through exposure to jealousy and envy. Otherwise justice would always be an abstraction for them. The failure of adults to assert their own pride meanwhile placed the blame on their shoulders, since what the young most needed were 'examples, even idols, among adults to carry responsibilities for them'.

> They neither need nor accept adults who shatter their image and authority. Human nature has yearned for a long time, if not from the start, for submission to authority.

Meaning what? That there is no pride without the overcoming of obstacles, or recognition without a fight for respect? That being handsome or clever is all good and well; yet that he or she granted these privileges should know that capitalizing on merits not yet deserved is like skating on the worthless path of least resistance? Objectives are needed, and adults should, above all, encourage daring. But there again: gains always come at the cost of losses. Such is life's law and order. Sooner or later, one pays for cheating, for laziness, for dishonesty with others and ultimately, or foremost, with oneself.

> Preachers of anti-authoritarian education propel kids from slippery grounds into precipices, because non-education, its logical heritage, produces psychological confusion, conductive to what Freud considered neurosis. Punishments appeal to individual dignity.
>
> The faith in oneself and one's ability to achieve something allows an only averagely gifted person to surpass himself where a much more gifted one would fail for lack of confidence.

Grounds for hope? Disappointingly, Bernhard Bueb is more

articulate in proposing solutions to problematic behaviour than in his analysis of their causes.

Why the magnetism of the forbidden? Why the thrill of transgression? Why the anger? Why the attraction to booze or drugs? Why the tendency to low-esteem?

By then, it was dinner-time (six-thirty). Like the previous night, a thunderstorm broke out.

Later I struggled to transfer the short stories 'Double' and 'Quit', on to a CD Rom for Dottore M to read, but failed miserably. Whereas a week ago I would have flown into a tantrum, I just figured I would solve the problem at some point tomorrow, and forgot about it. My eyes were tired to tears. Without feeling sad I was crying. The stories scorched my soul.

At nine o'clock, another of these infusions, during which I fell asleep . . . until eight the next morning. Magic!

Wednesday

For a restful change, Dottore M did the talking. He explained the term depression.

There are two main types of depression, the endogenous (internal, with possible genetic causes), and the extrogenous or reactive (caused by external causes such as mourning, accidents, in short, circumstantial events).

The first type generally speaking hits the hypersensitive, insecure, complex-ridden and above all, frustrated, who more often than not have communication difficulties.

The second type is less pathological (even though the effects are similar): it hits people who have failed in reaching some concrete objective, who encounter financial, professional or/and sentimental difficulties, or have been exposed to catastrophic events ranging from war, a fire, a flood, an accident, to excessive noise – the death of a loved one being one of the worst, naturally.

– Surprisingly, said Dottore M, post-traumatic stress only prevails in one to five per cent of cases. Many externally caused depressions heal by themselves, or with soft therapies based on relaxation, music, visual meditation or, simply, work and routine. Extrogenous depressions depend, to a large extent, on the reading of events, and there are always various possible hypotheses. The luckier ones have an innate ability to seek a positive, de-dramatizing interpretation. You may know the example of two prisoners looking outside from behind bars. One sees only the mud on the ground, the other sees the stars in the sky alone. In its endogenous form, which you seem affected by to a certain degree, disillusions or specific problems only act as triggers. They unleash a profound sense of failure, which is dormant, or latent, deep down and constantly. In other words, you have carried all your life the weight of a predisposition to depression, and keeping it at bay has required much nervous energy, which you gradually compensated, or generated, with alcohol. But instead of providing a counter-weight, it threw you off balance. The lack of a steady job, the separations from your husband, financial worries, to mention but the main causes, created the equivalent of what we medically call incubation.

I listened and repressed a tear or two. What was the matter with my eye-conduits? My soul.

– You have pulled the alarm-chord in time, contessa. You are intelligent enough to learn how to direct your train of thoughts and govern your behaviour mechanisms. An 'abandonic' or depressive personality is no fate. It is a problem that can be solved.

Good and well – but how? Dottore M stood up.

– Remember this: birds don't sing because they are joyous; they are joyous because they sing.

Then he was gone, and so was my sadness. I determined to practise singing and regain the energy to be – to make – happiness. Nevertheless, I didn't want to be alone. Downstairs I found the two persons I most wanted to see. Tonia instantly sensed (she is endowed with a sonar where empathy is concerned) that this was no time for a talk and suggested a game of ping-pong in the garden against Marco: she cannot herself play without breaking into floods of sweat . . . We laughed a lot. I lost as usual.

Later on, *atelier*: I started a beaded bracelet of glass pearls, as a present for Tonia. She is leaving next Sunday. A shame. She's sunshine.

I went on to the *Pankafit* class, a mixture of yoga and stretching. As in music therapy I was bored. All that nonsense about 'you are now reaching the centre of your omega' . . . . 'focus on your innermost soul' . . . 'reach out and in, exhale, inhale', followed by abundant *fffffffs*, *ohm-ohm-ohms* and more *fffffffs*, made me want to yawn rather than embrace the universe. The zen music, composed of wind breezes, waves lapping and bells tingling kept me alert for the simple reason I found it extremely unnerving.

There's a lot of breathing in the *Kama-Sutra* too, but definitely more action.

In the afternoon, at more or less the same time as before, gathered for another *Gruppo Fiabe*. But proceedings were too long to relate, and besides, were less animated that a few days ago. The tale had in fact been the chapter in *Alice's Adventures in Wonderland* that coined the expression 'grinning like a Cheshire cat'. Gianni had admonished Rick to stay seated after the latter made a move to leave the salon. Rick's withdrawn and hostile attitude puzzled me again. Afterwards, I asked Tonia if she knew anything about this strange teenager. She did, having overheard a conversation between his consultant doctor and a nurse in the 'closed section'. Apparently, surveillance of him had been reinforced, Rick being good at climbing walls and sneaking around noiselessly . . . like a cat. He was a cat hater. As a child, he poisoned them; later, he killed them; recently, he devised increasingly sophisticated torture techniques, a quick death no longer a satisfying outlet for his phobic hatred of the animals. It was feared he would escape and roam about implementing new escalations in cruelty.

Now his reaction to my 'cool cat' remark and his one and only utterance during the *Fiabe* made ominous sense. He had hissed that cats were an abortion of nature: 'I bet they grin, the greedy, useless bastards who give fuck-all in return. Ever heard of a guide cat helping the blind? Of cats rescuing a drowning man? Do sheepcats, guncats, hound cats, guard cats, police cats, husky cats or performing cats exist? No!' Rick practically yelled.

By some association to do with traumatic experiences, his hatred of cats must have extended to women, for, looking at *me*, he finished his tirade by saying that whereas dogs and men negotiate, cats and women smash what they cannot tear apart. If I began by responding with a smile, disliking cats with a passion myself, shudders now ran down my spine.

Tonia, unaware of my sudden terror, asked whether I considered myself a real, abusive alcoholic or an occasional one. While the latter drinks excessively on occasions, she explained, the former drinks steadily all the time. The answer was simple, and giving it diverted my mind from the thought of Rick's bulging eyes:

– I have, since that goddam menopause, become a real one. It followed the traditional sequence: social gatherings became drinking lunches or dinners; the tolerance level rose; the alibis became increasingly cunning; the first swig ever earlier and the last one, requiring an effort of the will – although, no. When I had enough, I had enough. I hardly drank at night, my body and mind having stored reserves.

– Did you get paralytic at times?

– On extremely few occasions. I'm a proud person and cautious not to appear ridiculous or undignified. I was also quite reasonable and absolutely every day drank a minimum of two big bottles of mineral water. I also ate normally, if little. Tonia, I really was a psychosomatic drinker in a compulsive way. Meaning, my brain demanded the stuff more than my blood needed it – there, it was pretty diluted. My craving for booze stemmed from a thinking pattern leading to a behaviour pattern. This really did suffuse me with torment, hence the typical day-and-night feelings of remorse, guilt, anxiety. For a year or so I haven't been able not to drink at all for one single day. But I very seldom had the shakes in the morning, or hangovers. There again, the effects of alcohol were more psychological: the failure to comply with good resolutions, the languor overcoming me in the afternoon, after the morning's nervousness, and finally the struggle to fall asleep without pills . . . a nightmare, Tonia.

– How long have you been aware of it being not only a habit but a problem turning into a disease?

– Long enough, that's to say, for too long, I sighed and shrugged.

– Did you hide to drink?

– No. I live alone anyway, most of the time.

– Yeah, she said with a hint of scepticism, but at other times?

– Not then either. My husband is not exactly moderate, and as for my friends, well . . .

I told her about the beautiful friend who came to prefer drinking companions to kindred souls. I didn't quite get the contradiction: boozers, when not hazardous shits, are usually much more compassionate than the average do-gooder.

– Darling, Tonia mused, you maybe stopped just in time.

Soothing as it was to hear this for the second time, it did not dislodge the image of Rick stalking me with complicated hooks and nail-studded whips, under a sky raining carcasses of cats and dogs, which crept up on me at regular intervals during that night. Nor did it erase the image of my passing out at Easter, instead of taking Robin and his daughters to the airport. (Which was worse? I could not say.)

Thursday

7 June

Today was some religious holiday here in the Tessino (the only Catholic canton in Switzerland). Therefore many activities were cancelled. Exactly one week has elapsed since my arrival. A small airline called Fly-Baboo (founded by a young entrepreneur whose dog is called Baboo) shuttles between Lugano and Geneva. I reserved my seat today and am relieved. However much I enjoy it here, another week will be enough – I pray. I may come back before Christmas to reinforce my hopefully recovered psychic and physical health, and to find out what might hopefully have changed.

I was allowed to take my cellular phone, as long as I wouldn't use it inside the clinic, but declined. I am beginning to resent the thing. People no longer accept one's being unreachable. Having to speak constantly while being 'on parole' shows the freedom this devilish device grants to be specious. Another addiction, as it were.

I called Robin from the telephone booth. Hearing his cheerful voice made me incredibly happy. When I told him I had won a game of ping-pong earlier, he exclaimed:

– The poor guy must really have been a beginner!

Maybe, but also an astrophysicist! Then I called my father; he was cheerful too. All was well, on a personal scale at least. Earlier I had, however, become aware of developments in Palestine.

With nothing to do, I retreated to some reading corner and found an amusing piece about Hollywood in the late thirties and early forties. The movie-mecca assembled the most disparate, talented English-speaking scriptwriters: Scott Fitzgerald, John Steinbeck, Irving Stone, Somerset Maugham, H. G. Wells, P. G.

Wodehouse, Graham Greene, Christopher Isherwood, George Bernard Shaw, William Faulkner. You might think they had a ball, but as the article explained at length, they were usually underpaid, given lousy offices and little recognition.

I came across two delectable quotes. The first was by David Niven: 'To be an actor it is essential to be an egomaniac, otherwise it just doesn't work. The supreme act of egomania is to sit down and write one hundred and thirty words about oneself. That I have already done in *The Moon's a Balloon*.'

The second was from James Hilton, a well-known scriptwriter in the late thirties: 'A writer must make his own reckoning as to whether he would rather say a little less exactly what he wants, to millions, or a little more exactly, to thousands.'

(Is this not what I am doing right now? Am I an egomaniac? People who are not well *do* tend to be narcissistic and to bang on and on . . .)

'Art therapy' was still on schedule. Like the music therapy, but unlike the *atelier* (which is merely meant as a creative occupation), this has a psychological purpose. You are asked to draw, paint or whatever you like. Your name must be affixed to the work.

I sat next to the man who arrived this morning, and with whom I had played ping-pong. To my stupefaction, by using watercolours on an A3 sheet he painted, without a moment's hesitation, the most astonishingly beautiful picture – two in one, in fact: through the middle of the sheet ran a river, with a bridge.

On the left side: an erupting volcano, a sun resembling a fireball, and underneath his name (Iñaki) in big, Japanese-looking calligraphy, and a chain of mathematical formulas, which from a distance looked like a serpentine line.

On the right side of the bending river: a peaceful and banal landscape in pale colours, a little house, trees, flowers, suspended in a dusky atmosphere.

Underneath it: his surname, in the same calligraphy, and small stars as a trademark.

Tonia and that elderly lady Reni, who had stood in front of her canvas like the figurehead of an ancient sailing ship (Reni, with her formulas such as, 'Nobody's perfect, but I'm not nobody,' or more dubious statements like, 'Depression is a meagre price to pay for not getting fat' – eyeing me as she said it) had both painted spirals. Tonia's was in cheerful colours, sprinkled with gold powder, and blurred; Reni's was much more structured, in dark shades of green, with an eye in the middle – a benevolent eye.

Marco had painted a landscape that would have seemed harmless enough, a typical garden in the summertime, had it not been for a purple, opaque cube in the bottom right-hand corner.

I have two left hands when it comes to trying to draw. I just cannot reproduce anything more complicated than a heart, a house or a tree. Observing my utter discouragement, especially as the others went about their tasks with facility and inspiration, then glancing at my miserable attempt to represent a pyramid and a felucca floating on the Nile, the art therapist came to my rescue and suggested a collage. She gave me scissors and magazines to cut out from.

After an hour precisely, she commanded us to stop, to sit in a circle, with our 'masterpieces' at our feet, and asked each of us in turn what we had meant to express.

Iñaki came first. As an astrophysicist, he had been beset by an existential crisis related to the acute emotional – compounding the intellectual – realization of man's insignificance, and he could not live with it. He quit his job and for three years has worked as a helper in humanitarian organizations, volunteering to go to places where wars, earthquakes or other disasters threaten human life. Only this year he has already been to Ghana, to Palestine and to Zimbabwe. So much for the left side of his painting. The peaceful right-hand side is where he feels most at home, in his Basque country house where he restores his energy and enjoys rare moments of peace – in sharp contrast to his work. He went on to say he no longer manages to cross the bridge. In peaceful surroundings, he feels guilty not to be where he could help; when in misery-stricken surroundings, he longs for homeliness. The reason why his friends and family insisted he spend some time here is for him to slow down, not feel the whole world's burden on his shoulders, while his mind is ablaze with images of death. He claimed not to be depressed, only utterly exhausted.

The psychologist very softly pointed out some asymmetries: an uncoloured spot on the bridge suggesting the structure might be damaged and therefore no longer crossable. We all asked Iñaki about the significance of the mathematical symbols, but by then he had chosen to retreat into his shell and spoke no more.

Enervating Reni mumbled about the eye being the window to the soul, the door to one's conscience, with eyelashes acting as curtains in front of circling reality. The psychologist merely remarked:

– One could also compare the image to a telescope. Could it be that you examine life and yourself a little too intensely?

Marco, as is his wont, made a long story short.

– I'm aware of the beauty and harmony around me, but can't enjoy it. I'm inside the cube. It is hermetic and dark. My wife and I are parting, mainly because I am afraid of my influence upon our small child, so I am shut out and feel blindfolded.

The psychologist said:

– Next week add windows and a door, will you?

-Maybe, answered Marco.

Tonia's explanation was simple:

– I needed to represent an open spiral because, having relapsed into toxicomania, I am aghast with fear that it could happen over and again.

– A spiral is by definition an open symbol, answered the art shrink, and so it should be. But nobody says the spiralling line can't be levelled out to follow an ascending, steady direction. You will be free to determine the perspective once you muster the strength to swirl from replication to replacement – meaning that conflicting behaviour patterns must *not* be made to co-exist, if the destructive one cannot be dislodged by the dynamic whose technical term is 'supersessionism' from the Latin for 'to sit upon'. Do you understand?

Tonia nodded, while the rest of us were nonplussed by this cryptic piece of advice.

Instead of commenting on my maladroit collage, the therapist (Beatrix was her name, I remembered at last) turned the sheet round to the dismal drawing of the pyramid and the felucca with oversized sails and simply said:

– Triangular relationships or situations seem to be the problem. We'll talk about it next week. Time is up.

I was deeply impressed by that man Iñaki. Funny thing is that, engaging in a short conversation, glad to meet someone who speaks Spanish, I found myself mixing up my pretty flawless Spanish with my improved Italian. I met Dottore M in the corridor and joked about it. He retorted very seriously:

– You know, it's quite good that we do this therapy mostly in Italian. When you can't speak a language fluently, you don't drift but get strait to the point. Right?

Now for an exciting event: I was allowed to go out for dinner with my great friend Lucca, who drove from Milan to see me. He was the one who recommended this clinic. Trying hard to look my best, but having packed only the strictly necessary, I was unlikely to win a *concours d'élégance*. But then isn't it my soul that men are interested in, hum?

Lucca, a born pessimist, was in the best of moods. He had won a vintage-car race and concluded a big deal. He took me to an absolutely lovely, romantic, rather pompous restaurant by the lake. Among the first courses, for instance, 'An *homage* to tomatoes with its scallop rainbow', written in five languages, Russian and Albanian included. (The owner is an Albanian gangster married to a Russian hooker, explained Lucca. Most pleasant people, he grinned.)

When I saw the wine glasses, my brain gave a tiny lurch. Then I forgot all about it, in spite of the bottle in its bucket between us. I did have an alcohol-free beer, though, and it tasted wonderful. I am fed up with drinking water, decaffeinated coffee and Diet Coca-Cola all day long.

On one occasion, Lucca, his wife and I had been invited out on the same boat. He had walked into my cabin to return a book, and found me struggling to open a nail-remover bottle with my teeth. 'Daaarling,' he had chuckled, 'now really! This is overdoing it. Can't you drink something *a trifle* softer?' We evoked the occasion with ambiguous irony.

The whole dinner was a success: not only because we had a thousand things to tell each other, but also – and this was truly important to me – because I made him laugh and felt animated; in short, the way I wish to be but fear I am not without recourse to drinks. Why this fear of being boring without stimulants? Hopefully the results of all the tests will light up my lantern on the subject.

Lucca drove me back. I rang the bell, was ushered in, said thank you and good night, then headed for the stairs as a peremptory voice barked:

– Just a minute. Follow me.

I had to take an alcohol test! Since when did I last register zero point zero? I mused, amused.

What a marvellous day, though! Why can't it be so more often? Could my erratic self have something to do with it, dear Watson? I went to bed feeling better than I had in months, if not years.

Friday

8 June

The sun has come out at last, and even the temperature rose. It's been damn cold so far. This morning a nurse who particularly likes me brought me a big coffee can instead of a small one. She is the only one who lets me swallow the pills she brings without watching me before leaving the room. Such small bendings of rules are meaningful, illicit treats in this clinical routine.

Dottoressa D walked in shortly afterwards. She's in charge of the more affective matters, whereas Dottore M mostly deals with dependency and addiction.

I had already talked quite extensively about my father and Robin. The *dottoressa* half-jokingly pointed out how many similarities they had in terms of personality and outlook.

– I know, I responded. My mother, who never misses a beat to be acid, told me I was marrying my father moments before our wedding – during which her mood wasn't particularly uplifting, I may say.

– It is precisely your mother I would like you to tell me more about today.

How can one be fair, when being so angry? I tried, and set about telling her how, to the best of my belief, my mother had quite a happy childhood until the war. Music played an important part, and she has been a passionate *aficionado* ever since. But during the war, she lost her father, to whom she felt much closer than her mother. Her elder brother went missing. When Dresden, where she was brought up on stern protestant principles, was erased from the map in 'forty-five, she and her mother fled with only a few suitcases to a small town in northern Germany. There her aunt owned two houses, so at least they weren't roofless and the town was pleasant enough. Naturally, her mother never ceased hoping her son would be found. He had been her favourite child. My mother and grandmother possessed, I think, a bittersweet relationship. The latter was an intellectual, authoritative, quite formidable woman, even in physical stature. While my paternal grandmother, who also lost a son, imbued my father with a complex about not being tall enough (meaning, not as tall as his elder brother), my maternal grandmother imbued her daughter with a complex about not being over-intelligent. She's resented this all her life and has spent most of it trying to impress on others how well read and clever she is. Rarely did I witness her saying, 'I have no idea,' whatever the subject.

Anyway, she grew into a stunning beauty: jade-coloured eyes, dark hair, a sensual mouth and a lovely smile. She became a physiotherapist, I cannot remember why. From all I heard, she was a vivacious young woman back then, and a notorious flirt.

Aged twenty-three or thereabouts, she married a Gary Cooper look-alike with a taciturn edge. Were they happy during their two years together? He had some acute disease, suffered probably more than he ever admitted, thought it was incurable; and when my mother came home one evening, she found him dead. A gruesome death, like all suicides, but the choice of gas poisoning, so soon after that war, made it even more morbid. How my mother reacted and recovered I do not know. What I could vividly imagine, and with infinite compassion, were the infernal interrogations that must have plagued her, amplifying her despair.

In those days, one had to get on with life to survive. Friendships became all the stronger through the feeling of solidarity that prevailed. With most families having lost practically everything, sources of entertainment were simple: picnics, long walks in the mountains, a bottle of wine or a new bicycle provided the elation people later sought from 'artificial paradises' or other more or less perverse games with fire.

But enough drifting, as Dottore M would say.

Two years later, she met my father. It would seem it was love at first sight, at least on his part. Things moved fast. They were married only months later, with the lukewarm consent of my paternal grandmother, an old-fashioned aristocrat, who considered her future daughter-in-law's family too *bourgeois*. Was my mother in love? My father was good-looking, amusing, brilliant and well-off. On the other hand, he too had health problems: heavy allergies and a manifest penchant for drinking. Did she, unconsciously or not, determine to 'save' this man after failing to save another?

Were *their* first years of marriage happy? I was later told they contemplated a separation but discarded it when my mother learnt she was pregnant with me.

When I was three years old, they moved to Paris, my father having been offered an interesting professional proposition. The first nine years there were happy ones all in all, though there was much fighting between my parents – because of alcohol. Towards me each of them was loving, and I adored them both.

I was also happy in the school I was sent to: the teachers, the fact it was international and its 'Only one race, the human race' ethos. I made some friends, but not many. I was rather introverted and solitary. Already my refuge was reading. Aged twelve, when my favourite books were detective stories, I noticed how my mother would write for hours, dictionary to hand, tear up her drafts and start again. One day I pieced some of the scraps of paper together. It was an ardently passionate letter, obviously not addressed to my father. *That* discovery changed *my* life.

I paused in my narration, with the feeling of being hampered by a blockage.

– Must I go on? I asked wearily

– Please do, the *dottoressa* said.

– Can't we change the subject?

– No, Aleana. Skipping from one thought to another, if possible an unrelated one, is what we do all the time when we encounter an obstacle. My job is to help you stand in front of it, observe it, wriggle or drill yourself through it, and eventually to surmount it. You will see, if you manage once, you'll manage twice, and get the drift. The past looks brighter from the other side.

She was right, I guess. I had carefully stashed painful memories away and built a wall around them. Retrieving what had been maladroitly or cunningly hidden was difficult, unpleasant and painful.

– All right, I said. Just as I was beginning to feel sorry for my mother, looking so tired and vulnerable, she abruptly changed register and started to put the blame for her chagrin and infidelity on my father. She harped on his character failings, his sexual indifference, and naturally ended her litany by pillorying his drinking excesses. That did it. Had I been able to walk out of the house there and then I would have done just that. Instead I retreated to my room, and thereafter into minimal communication. Cuddling times were over. She felt and resented being judged by one who had neither the right nor the maturity to do it, complaining to everybody how difficult I had become. She was right, of course – but at the wrong time.

From that day on, our relationship has been strained. I started pleading with my father to be sent to a boarding school, using the foxy argument that I needed to learn to live in a community, and other perhaps contorted but efficient ones. He gave in, with a bleeding heart, I imagine, for I was a source of joy in his life.

(At this point the tale about the king letting his daughter go and seek luck elsewhere crept into my mind.)

There followed two of the happiest years of my life. I was accepted into a Swiss school, again one where about fifty nationalities and God knew how many religions were represented. The headmaster was a colonel. Teachers were fabulous, classes small, the sites magnificent.

One weekend my mother and father came to visit me. We drove to a restaurant by a lake, and suddenly a most violent disagreement erupted. My mother had disapproved of that boarding school all along, on the grounds that it was famous for the wrong reasons (among the Rosey alumni, the Shah of Iran, Rainier of Monaco, all sorts of Niarchoses and Rockefellers) and that, being too spoilt in the first place, it was the mistaken one for me. What initiated the dispute over lunch on that occasion, and why it degenerated from bad to worse, I simply could not remember. Conclusion: we drove back to the hotel we were staying in – the Hôtel de la Paix! My mother rushed off in a flurry, soon to return with her suitcase and announce she was leaving my father for good and all. He and I were sitting in the hall, sipping tea. He remained impassive. This disconcerted her, but after a melo-dramatic spin, she whirled away – having taken the precaution of asking the concierge for a taxi to the station in the loudest of voices . . . After a long while, I murmured that perhaps this was all for the best. Their marriage was not harmonious, I had seen him miserable too often and after all, at fifty-two, a man could start a whole new life again, couldn't he? My father smiled weakly. After another long pause, he stood up and said: 'I'm going to fetch your mother.' *That* decision changed *his* life.

Knocking back two glasses of water, my throat dry from all the talking, I told the *dottoressa*:

– Now comes the last straw; then I'll stop, because I'm drained.

In the evening we had been invited for dinner at some relatives' house. When my parents returned from the station, I expected them to say we wouldn't go. Far from it. My mother barked that I must get dressed properly for dinner, and fast. There were a dozen guests round the table, and to my utter amazement she behaved as her usual mundane self, as if nothing at all had happened, even making an extra effort to deploy charm (though not wit, of which she is devoid). My father, on the contrary, was unusually and, to me, understandably subdued. At some point, I bumped into my mother.

'How do you do it?' I couldn't help snapping.

'You like money?' she snapped back. 'Well, so do I.'

Not only cuddling times but also respect ebbed there and then to bygone days.

– Now, dear *dottoressa*, a fag is a must.

Before she left the room she gave me a quick hug.

I smoked slowly, watching the lake, and feeling equally blue. Then I dozed, the way people too exhausted to sleep do. Yet I woke up full of energy: sleep purifies.

In the afternoon I went to the centre of Lugano with another lovely patient here, a Turkish lady in her early forties, with the most open, kind, almost radiant face you could imagine (her traits could be Thai). We had taken an instant liking to each other.

Gilda wanted to buy shoes; I needed a pair of trousers. We strolled through the sunny streets, chatting gaily about this and that. I found not only what I was looking for, but also a sexy blouse to match. She found the perfect shoes, so we were both in the best of moods. If it cannot be diamonds, shopping does the job as a girl's best friend. Then we sat on a terrace, and she told me her story – certainly not in the evasive way typical of first conversations.

Alcohol again, but in a big way, and for about four years. It reached a point where she no longer went to bed; at dawn she'd drop spreadeagled on the floor. On a binge she would swallow down four or so bottles of wine before the so-called 'happy hour', of which none were left. As happens with many alcoholics, she became anorexic and skeletal. She could turn physically violent at times, and even steal things, though she's obviously loaded (she has occupied the only private suite in the clinic for nearly three months). When you hear such a catalogue of collapses from the mouth of such a sweet and smiling person, you wonder . . .

– When did it start? I asked. And why?

– Well . . . I was overprotected for too long, living in my parents' beautiful house by the Bosporus, partying, being driven by a chauffeur and all that. Still, I studied fashion design and decided to go to Paris. That was a fiasco: I hated it but learnt something. Then, six years ago, I moved to Milan. There I had a break-through. I designed two successful collections, and began to become known. But the third one turned out a flop, and the press to be unsupportive. My protector – also my financial backer – let me down. At that stage I discovered a choleric facet of my personality that scared me. I started drinking quite a bit to calm my nerves. Then I was drinking even more to regain enough confidence to design another collection. Working at night, under the influence of alcohol, I believed I was a genius. The morning after I'd tear up what was actually delirious rubbish.

She sighed, still smiling.

– I know what you mean, Gilda. The same has happened to me when writing. It's awful.

– Well . . . then I stopped sketching and drawing altogether, and met the wrong group of people, the so-called *jeunesse dorée*. While I desperately tried to hang on to my dreams, they didn't seem to have any, other than killing time in an enjoyable way. Since I had lots of money, I threw parties, invited them to weekends in Portofino and all that. This certainly was one of the reasons they so readily accepted me, but they also made me feel old. Most of them were much younger, you see. I claimed to be thirty when in fact I was thirty-seven, Istanbul time. Generally speaking, I started to lie a lot. Fantasy seemed a convenient balsam beneath which to soothe my scathing sense of failure. It went downhill from there. Sleeping around, dancing wildly through the nights when not crashing out. Finally I went to see a doctor. Not only was my mind deranged, but my liver damaged. He recommended this clinic with its high reputation for personal attention, individual care and general peacefulness. So here I am. Dottore M tells me I could leave, but I'm scared. Here I am being overprotected again, so it's a home from home and all that.

She smiled again, like an apologetic child.

– I have become a bit of a 'previror', you know? Like those people who undergo DNA tests and become too much aware of genetic risks of cancer? Then they become excessively cautious, almost cripples, in the emotional or the physical sense. I am haunted by my weakness and all that. Others undergo prophylactic surgery, or change their lifestyle radically . . . I cocoon in comfort, you know? Are you also scared of going back to your familiar surroundings?

– No, sweetie. I won't fall into the same old traps, for obvious health reasons, plus my need to write clear-headedly. I never thought twice before crossing the street, and never will be able to. Not in my character, or DNA if you prefer. But mainly, I *want* to wake up in the morning feeling proud instead of despising myself, bemoaning the abdication of my will-power. Guilt is a vampire. Shame is a killer.

Second Weekend

Saturday, 9 June

As usual, writing in the morning; after lunch, more writing and, for the first time, some sun-bathing. In the *atelier* I started a big collage. I am getting the drift of it. It allows the juxtaposition of images and words, contrasts and contradictions, coded messages and also some poetry.

A small group of us watched the ladies' finale of the Roland Garros French Open tennis, but this year I cannot get excited about the whole thing. Justine Henin was bound to win, so is Nadal tomorrow. The latter should be my favourite, coming from Majorca, but since he grew into a superstar, I find he has lost his modesty and the youthful charm of wonderment. Back in my room, I sorted my papers and found a letter my father sent me a year ago which I had Scotch-taped in my bathroom but then included in the folder I brought with me. I'll translate a few thoughts left by Theresa de Ávila (1515–82) that he quoted.

Oh Lord,

Preserve me from the delusion that I have something to say on each and every subject.

Deliver me from the big temptation to want to put order into other people's lives. Teach me to be reflective but not too inward looking, helpful but not dictatorial.

Having gained so much wisdom, it seems a pity not to transmit it, but you understand, my Lord, that I want to retain some friends.

Preserve me from the accumulation of endless details, and help me come to the point.

Teach me to remain silent about my ailments and concerns.

They increase and therewith the desire to tell about them.
Teach me the marvellous wisdom that I am allowed to be mistaken.
I do not wish to be a saint, since life with saints is so difficult – but an old embittered person is a devilish creation.
Teach me the gift to discover hidden talents in others and give me the beautiful capacity, oh Lord, to help these persons recognize them.

What did I do next? I went to the smoking salon and lectured a twenty-eight-year-old, fat but graceful girl, sitting alone, melancholic as usual. Raquel is here to cure a depression caused by her failure to help her boyfriend give up drugs: 'co-dependency'. I like her a lot. She told me she had just been talking to him on the phone. I had guessed as much. So I said:

– Look, why persist with calling that guy. You are here because of *him*. What does *he* do meanwhile? Getting stoned into a stupor. You are your own priority, Raquel. There are other men. There's a bright future out there. Why not try to distance yourself from that self-destructive character? He'll survive. Either he decides to deal with his problem, or else he'll find another victim who'll mother him. *Animos!* You're lovely, and so is life, if you decide so. Generous as you are, you deserve all the happiness!

Theresa of Ávila would not have been impressed. But Raquel said, 'Thank you.'

Sunday, 10 June

Today, no doctors, no activities, no nothing. The sun shone and I lay on the chaise-longue learning by heart some of Rudyard Kipling's poem 'If '.

> If you can keep your head when all about you
> Are losing theirs and blaming it on you;
> If you can trust yourself when all men doubt you,
> But make allowance for their doubting too;
> If you can wait and not be tired of waiting,

Or being lied about, don't deal in lies,
Or being hated, don't give way to hating,
And yet don't look too good, nor talk too wise; . . .

If you can talk with crowds and keep your virtue,
Or walk with Kings – nor lose the common touch,
If neither foes nor loving friends can hurt you,
If all men count with you, but none too much;
If you can fill the unforgiving minute
With sixty seconds' worth of distance run,
Yours is the Earth and everything that's in it,
And – which is more – you'll be a man, my son!

Tonia walked into my room to say goodbye. I gave her the beaded bracelet I had assembled for her. She burst out laughing and pulled out a bracelet she had done for me. From among dozens of shades we had chosen the same colours, turquoise and lavender blue. We put them around each other's wrists, and sealed the knot by burning it with a match. I was sad about her leaving, but she was radiant. I suspected something, correctly: Marco and Tonia had sneakily spent her last night together. They had seemed so attuned and caring these last ten days, that the happy end – or rather beginning – came as no big surprise.

They even made plans, among which was spending August in Crans-Montana, where he owns a chalet. I am invited any time, to stay as long as I wish, she insisted. What a good idea! I had intended to escape from the crowd and the heat anyway.

Teasingly, I asked Tonia if Marco wasn't a bit too intellectual for her. She had told me before of a two-year affair with a Chilean, adding that he was stupid. She then went out with some Italian, whom she described as primitive. I had wondered why she fell for such men.

– You know, Aleana, I have to empathize and talk all day long at work, so I enjoyed the animal instincts! Besides, they made me feel more intelligent than I actually am!

– But Marco is extremely clever. Not too drastic a change?

– He can be quite a beast too, she giggled and twinkled. And then he's just as bi-polar as I am. I spend my life trying to understand others, as psychiatrists must, but am not used to *the feeling* of being understood. Perhaps I wanted to forget myself, hence my choice of guys and the self-induced blackouts. In any case, it's a fabulous new experience.

– I'm so glad for the both of you! Just as well he's separating from his wife . . . When will you see each other again?

– He stays another three weeks, but made me promise neither to call, nor to visit.

– He must be very sad.

– Sad? Don't know . . . But he had an anxiety attack early this morning and started screaming full pitch. Two nurses came at once and found us stark-naked on the bed.

– Christ! I exclaimed.

– No, his half-brother, remember?

We clapped a 'give me five'.

– You know what? It wasn't a problem. One of them said we made a beautiful couple, while the other gave him an injection. Then they were gone without further ado.

– Amazing!

– I told you: this is a special place and we all are damn lucky. This morning we were summoned for a hell of a reprimand though!

– Do you want me to keep him company once in a while? Walking around, playing ping-pong, whatever?

– By the way! What *do* you do to people, darling? I went to say goodbye to Raquel and found her singing in front of the mirror, putting on make-up for the first time since I've been here. When I asked what was going on, she said: 'It's Aleana. She said things I had heard before, but in a special way. I made decisions. I'm going to take care of myself and learn to be my own priority, as she put it.' Then I went to see Gilda. She usually sleeps till noon, but there she was, wearing a dress, which she never does, cutting patterns on a cardboard mannequin. 'What's the matter with *you*?' I asked. 'Oh, you know, I went downtown with Aleana the other day, and talking to her, I sort of snapped out of my despondency. Yesterday I went to buy scissors, materials and all that, and now I'm going to get on with it, just as she spends her mornings writing.' On the way to your room, I met Freddy, all excited because I had told him a guy from Milan picks me up in a fast car. When I said I was on my way to say goodbye to you, he went, '*Che carina!*' with starry eyes. You should work here! Anyway – yes: it would be nice if you spent a little time with Marco. He likes you too.

Whereupon the phone rang, her friend (the stupid one, the primitive, or another rampant male?) was downstairs, so off she rushed after a strong embrace.

I wondered whether to go for a walk along the lake. Lugano combines the best of Switzerland (everything works) and of Italy, on the opposite shore: people have the Latin laid-backness, music streams out of doors and windows, amiability comes from the heart and everyone seems to be in a good mood. The old town, festooned with hanging flowers and flags (a regatta is soon to take place) is very picturesque – as is the picture-postcard panorama. But I was lazy. Doing nothing is sometimes best (a principle I had often evoked, though condoning an unhealthy torpor was totally unrelated to my present relaxation) .

Later on I reflected idly on what Tonia had said, and envied her. All in all, my sex-life has been one long yawn. In none too prudish a life, I can count more fingers on one hand than lovers with whom I have experienced 'the imploding kick'. Tonia is luckier, being the quick-big-bang type. It simplifies matters.

Naturally, I once felt much curiosity, mainly to discover what all the fuss was about. My awakenings were promising, as my skin responded enthusiastically to caresses. But then the real thing happened, and if first experiences are anything to go by, mine was a hilarious flop. It happened with the elder brother of a girl-friend, a banal scenario. No delicacy here; the guy went straight to the point. He then lay back with a smirk and asked:

– How was I?

– Compared to *what*?

– Not to worry, whatever-he-was called benignly answered.

He then peeled off a layer of his skin. I gaped with horror. A fraction of a second later, he was up and dressed, not looking particularly scalped. Age fifteen, I had not the faintest idea what a condom was.

Time has passed. What turns me on, I discovered, is the fugitive, the tentative, the beginnings, the delicate tiptoeing towards a climax undulating like a wave rather than exploding like thunder. I have shivered and shaken to the core of every fibre feeling the tip of a finger against my spine or the brush of lips in the hollow of my neck. Given the choice between penetration and foreplay, I choose games any time. Eroticism is what I fantasize about; without it, sex is a bore. I have faked burns and bruises while freezing, or while thinking of my car needing petrol and my chicken-curry innovations. No doubt I have missed out on a lot of fun and fire – above all, on fulfilment. I have blamed myself for it for most of my life. Well . . . not entirely true. Although the saying, according to which there are no frigid women but only lousy lovers, has been widely documented, the same specialized literature advises one to indicate what to do and when, as if the body were a road map, its sensitivity an alarm clock. Some men would perfunctorily oblige; but what kind of pleasure is to be derived from such mechanical politeness? There were the few and far betweens who instinctively knew how to make it click. I call them my lesbian Lucys, for reasons I shall not dwell upon. The bottom line is that I am blocked in some kind of psychosomatic impasse I might investigate when the most urgent matters are dealt with. However, if the body has its language – and should I be as hopeless in decrypting it as in sending messages – perhaps I should contemplate other realms of harmony, seeking inspiration from the 'Music Monk', who is happily entwined with an elation of his own.

The solution being out of immediate grasp but a Diet Coke within it, I went downstairs, passed the salon where Rick and his watchdog-nurse seemed riveted by *The Aristocats*, *Top Cat*, *Felix* or *Fritz the Cat,* and returned to my room, missing Tonia. Another thunderstorm was deploying into a mesmerizing spectacle.

Monday

Another sunny day, adding to my feeling of well-being again at last. I went to sit on the veranda, where I met a forlorn-looking Gilda. No smile in sight, an alarming symptom on her normally endlessly smiling face.

– What's the matter, *chérie*?

– I decided to prolong my stay in the clinic again, until mid-July.

She had been due to leave at the end of this month, and though apprehensive, seemed to look forward to being reunited with her family.

My critical mind, which I *must* learn to keep in check, induced me to surmise that Gilda simply lacked the guts to face the music, the 'real world' outside, having installed herself in some sort of infantile immaturity, like curling up on a comfortable sofa.

– Why? Anything happened?

– I can't do it. I can't.

– Do what?

– Sketch. Invent. Visualize. Get inspired. I nearly smashed my mannequin into pieces out of frustration last night. I didn't, but destroyed my patterns instead. My choleric facet, remember? Without alcohol, I have neither fantasy nor confidence. For the first time in three months, I felt the craving again. My hands were shaking.

– But Gilda, don't despair! After a long gap, it's perfectly normal to have trouble getting back in motion in every sense. Persevere! Who said life would be easy anyway?

It brought back a display of her perfectly capped teeth, but the smile didn't extend to her eyes. She asked:

– How's your writing going?

– Listen, I enjoy it and firmly believe I write a lot better without drinking, but bear in mind that it requires no sparking fantasy. I keep to a kind of diary, meaning I merely relate impressions, events, thoughts 'and all that'. It's a lot easier than anything you try to do.

– May I read some of it?

Other than the 'Cat Hater', Gilda is the only one here who speaks fluent English.

– No, I answered. Sorry.

– Am I in it?

– Yes. As the loveliest, most artistically talented person I have met here! I even describe the fantastic half-drawing, half-collage you did in art therapy.

A blatant lie, since I forgot to do so. But the work was impressive. The psychologist had remarked that her silhouettes, rather foetus-like at first, were becoming erect and proud, concluding that this indicated an excellent progress.

– Would you do me a favour? she asked, in the shy way that makes her so endearing

– Sure. What favour?

– Would you come and write in my room? I don't want to be alone.

Her room being a suite in which I had spotted a large table, it was easy to set up my computer. I noticed a large number of books on a corner shelf I hadn't noticed the first time.

– You read a lot, don't you?

– Oh yes, she beamed. A bit of everything, mainly novels though. Do you know what I started doing lately?

– How should I? I smiled.

– Ever heard of 'book leaving'?

– No.

– Nor had I until reading an article about it. It consists of leaving in a public place, with your name and address written on the first page, a book you really, *really* liked. The idea is that it will, perhaps, be picked up and read by a person who'll also really, *really* like it, and who will get in touch with you. I left many books (not my own, I bought second copies) on benches in gardens or streets. To no avail, you know? That goes to illustrate how lonely I have felt, she sighed, adding unexpectedly after a moment:

– Lots of money can be an isolating shield, even a carapace. Too many options, not enough obligations, and all that.

– Might be, I sighed in turn. But I wish I had more of it. Constantly worrying about expenses is no fun either. When I went to Gstaad this winter, for instance, I couldn't invite friends, give beautiful presents or take taxis instead of buses after dark. I didn't even ski. Renting the whole equipment, plus buying the lift pass, was simply beyond my means. The snow conditions were dismal, mind you, so it wasn't a problem. Still . . .

She remained silent for a while, looking at me. I thought: Yes – yes. I look pretty well off. Partly because I have the fitting accessories and props, Hermes belts, a Rolex watch, etcetera. Mainly because I also have – no pretence – that 'touch of class' the French call, for reasons that always eluded me, *du chien*: 'dog-ness'!

– Darling Aleana, when you come to Istanbul with your father, I will spoil you, take my word for it. We'll have lots of fun!

My father and I are indeed planning to spend ten days in Istanbul in September. The plane tickets were my Christmas plus birthday present this year. It has been his unfulfilled dream for a long time to visit Constantinople and then for the first time see the site of the battle at Gallipoli. I had told Gilda about it.

– Thank you, I said.

– Thank *you* for keeping me company!

– It's a pleasure. But the deal is: you draw while I write, okay?

– Yes, she smiled, eyes included.

– Just one more thing, Gilda. Would you allow me to take your collage when I leave, as a souvenir?

– No, she answered in a whisper. I am not happy with it yet.

She burst into a pearly laughter I hadn't heard from her before.

– You know something? I haven't said 'No' for ages! It feels damn good!

We worked for two hours, with a violin concerto for background. I adore violin concertos more than any other kind of classical music. I then returned to my room, Dottoressa D having said she'd be in to see me around two o'clock.

The *dotoressa* had a determined look on her face as she told me without preamble that she wanted to return to the subject of my mother and get it out of the way. That last bit sounded the best.

– Forgive me for insisting, but it is important. Your mother is. We left it at the disastrous weekend in Geneva when you were still at school.

I was prepared for that, having expected as much.

– Right, I said, and launched straight in. A year later I graduated, in fact I managed to get the best baccalaureate for years in that institution. Needless to say there was lots of luck involved and it took ammunition away from my mother's vitriolic imprecations about the place. The exams were state exams, taken across the border, so no preferential treatment could be invoked. Since I had skipped a class for reasons too long to explain and irrelevant here, I was barely seventeen when I graduated. Too young, my parents agreed upon for a change, to live on a campus. Thanks to Mr Morales, my unforgettable Argentinian teacher at the school (he committed suicide by lying on a railway track, after finding out his wife had betrayed him, as one of his predilected literary heroes had done), I became totally fascinated with Hispanic literature and culture in general. It was decided I would spend a gap year as a paying guest in the vast flat of an impoverished *marqués* in Madrid, and enrol in the university, mainly to improve my Spanish.

That November Franco died, students rebelled against the censorship and other musty laws. In short, I studied little but had the best of times: good, clean fun. By chance the other two paying guests were Spanish, one from Santander, the other from Tenerife.

We got along super well and they introduced me to their friends. I often wrote to my parents, ecstatically describing the way of life for families composed more often than not of five to seven brothers and sisters, whisky-drinking fathers and loving, tolerant mothers: in other words, a sane environment. My mother took it personally, as you can imagine. During my years in school (apart from the aforementioned weekend in the Hôtel de la Paix), it was my father alone who came to visit once in while. Same in Madrid.

(I paused, remembering the occasion when he had allowed me to invite a group of friends to dinner, then to a night club. He had a ball and was not displeased to find they had good manners and prestigious surnames, nor that the pretty girls demurely demonstrated how wonderful they found him. At three o'clock in the morning, after vase-sized drinks, we left the place. In front of the door stood a wrinkled old gipsy, holding a basket full of roses. With gallant intentions and great panache, my father announced: 'I'd like to buy the whole basket. Do you take American Express?' Our explosion of mirth took a long time to abate. This anecdote being beside the point, I left it aside and returned to the subject at hand.)

My mother felt left out, as so often happens in triangular relationships. My father and I had always been on the same wavelength, and the passing of years only reinforced our complicity and mutual trust. Rejection is torture, as we have all experienced at one time or another, but with my mother, where her rapport with me was concerned, it happened most of the time. Whenever we saw each other, I was on the defensive, which offended her. But she acted very sourly, and any achievement of mine only seemed to irritate her further. I gather she considered, 'I had it all too easy.' To my own surprise, I had been accepted at the London School of Economics – quite difficult of access with its worldwide repute – and honourably graduated in Modern History. At the same time, I had fun and boyfriends. Being as readily accepted by fellow students on a scholarship as by the offspring of dukes, I led a life of contrasts.

(I felt tears, those bloody tears bubbling out of a mixture of anger and regret, surface behind my eyes again. They remained there: I won.)

My mother did contribute, to a significant degree, to enable me to buy a small but cosy flat, by cutting into her share of a none too bountiful inheritance. My grandmother had died. I had shown little grief, even though, to this day, I often think of her with infinite tenderness. Back then, I was selfishly busy. I was studying hard, since, fun notwithstanding, it was a demanding curriculum and a tough challenge . . .

(I paused again, hoping for some feedback. In vain. I was growing bored with the sound of my own voice.)

The *dottoressa* needed no heavy brainstorming before she asked:

– Do you think your mother envies you?

– That might have been the problem ever since I left *her* for boarding school, I admitted.

I was privileged, I was becoming, if not a stunning beauty, pretty in a striking way. I gained confidence, recovered my gaiety, made friends easily and not only had good grades but great boyfriends on top, so to speak! When I was in Munich, twice or thrice a year, the telephone would ring a lot, and sometimes so would the doorbell, with flowers addressed to . . . me! While still in London, I was official girlfriend to Archie, one of the most successful, handsome, witty and intriguing men at the time. When she came to stay at his weekend house, his lack of reverence debased her. Once again, she felt 'left out', as the rest of the party, myself included, laughed at our in-jokes, talked about the same books, and went around doing whatever we pleased, the only common ritual being drinks followed by meals. She was not the centre of attention, and resented it; and I have to confess I never distracted her by suggesting walks or excursions, for instance.

Two other factors compounded her bitterness, the first being that many of my parents' friends had begun to treat me as an equal and no longer as 'the daughter of'. I was stealing the show unawares. The second and worst was the fact of ageing. Her being years older than her French lover certainly didn't help. Neither did having been, in the true sense, a beauty. She spent excessive time in front of mirrors, be it in her bathroom, at the hairdresser or buying clothes. At too early a stage, I think, she lamented what she saw: the first signs of losing the battle against gravity. She soon waged a campaign of her own, resorting to injections and discreet surgery. But her figure was a problem: she inherited her mother's tendency to overindulge in sweets and put on weight. On the beach, she'd constantly ask: 'I'm not as fat as *that* one, am I?' She had famously beautiful legs – quite aside from her spectacular eyes. But again: there I was, slim to the point of androgyny – but curvaceous – and my turquoise eyes not going unnoticed either. She had been thirty when I was born: when I was in my twenties she was therefore in her fifties, and almost thirty years ago that was perceived as the beginning of the decline for women. Do you follow me?

– I do, smiled the *dottoressa*. Things changed. Nowadays, a woman at fifty is still desirable, she dresses more or less like her daughters, *insoma*, a kind of decade-displacement has taken place, thanks to better diets, cosmetics, whatever.

I was pleased to hear that, and even more pleased when she consulted not her biological clock but her watch before asking:

– How did things develop?

– Bah. Was she hit by a menopausal depression like me? I now wonder – too late. Be that as it may, she had more lovers (*she* told me so, why, I never understood) and our communication followed in spurts and bounds. Occasionally, we would talk with ease and confidence. Yet I was repeatedly hurt by the way she manipulated, then misused my trust. Whatever I told her would rebound like a boomerang in the form of venomous arrows at opportune moments. I never left a letter or anything personal lying around, certain she would feel no scruples over scrutinizing whatever it might be. Age has exacerbated her already very short fuses. She tends to wake up on the left foot, perhaps she was born on it . . . In short I feel she can't stand my guts, to put it bluntly. I irritate her.

She believes I'm light-headed and over-loved. She thinks I'm tough – or at least that's what I think she thinks – and would not find it unfair if my good-fortune deserted me. Marrying Robin was *le comble*: he was the most eligible, once-again-bachelor in town – not for some volatile wealth, but because of his charm, wit, name and good nature. And who does he *fall* for? Me. He shows her no exaggerated affection either, aware that she has caused much damage. So the answer to the question – is my mother envious – is yes.

– Does she have many friends?

– My *parents* have plenty, all over the world. My mother . . . well, she's a man's woman. She craves adulation as we all need oxygen. Deep down she was always insecure and the waning of her beauty makes being admired more vital to her than ever. She surpasses herself as a hostess, she is always elegant and an attentive listener. However, her penchant for moralizing and being severe about everyone but herself does annoy some of her entourage. Her lady friends tend to be older, less 'polished', far from beautiful and afflicted by problems or illnesses. With them she is the kindest-hearted, most helpful person you could meet.

Dottoresa D stood up, at last. But there was one last thing I needed to add:

– A year ago exactly I started a therapy with a psychologist in Palma. Alice is lovely and warm, but as you could deduce from the entangled state in which I arrived here, it didn't do much of a trick. She achieved one thing, however: to relegate my mother to the back of my mind – at least until now. A nasty, galvanizing exchange at dinner in a restaurant last November made me write my mother a long letter after Christmas. It stated, in essence, that I was by now old enough to claim the right to choose whom I would allow to hurt me. I had stomached, or overreacted to enough abuse and decided to un-hook myself. 'That you say what you say and behave the way you do is your prerogative. The way I respond is mine, and I will no longer respond. Please let us make a truce for a while, in the hope it may lead to peace one day.'

– How did she react to that?

– She did not wait or weigh her words: she wrote me an almost illegible letter, full of deleted words, and harsh ones. Since she doesn't forgive, is unable to forget, the chain of reproaches led back to a very distant past. It was also the letter of a distraught mother whom I had robbed of the joys of being a grandmother. *Voilà*.

I stood up too, looking forward to getting on with my collage. They really do have a point with that 'activity': concentrating on creative, manual tasks sweeps your mind clear.

Before leaving, the *dottoressa* said in a somewhat sad voice:

– I also had an extremely damaging relationship with my mother. Next time, I will spare you the talking, and if you allow, propose my conclusions and advice.

Therapy makes one realize how umbilical one is. Not only was I grateful that the *dottoressa* spared me the horoscope nostrums or greetings-card formulas, but also that once in a while she opened up too, however fleetingly. This once, I felt like giving her a short hug, and did.

As we started toiling away in the *atelier*, another violent thunderstorm broke with gushy winds and hail. I rushed out, ran downstairs and called Lisa in Geneva.

– How's the weather there? I panted.

– Apocalyptic! she answered, wondering what this short and snappy call was all about.

Little did she know that Hugo's flight to London was due to take off that very moment (she is a good friend of his). I felt a lump in my throat. For some obscure reason, I was terrified something might happen – perhaps because a few days earlier I read about Carole Lombard's death. She had hurriedly decided to take a plane instead of a train from Vegas to Los Angeles, impatient to be reunited with her husband, Clark Gable. The aircraft exploded.

Once more, I marvelled at the soothing psychological effect of concentrating on handicraft. After what seemed a very long time,

I came back to my room, and found a text message on my mobile: 'Well arrived. xxx'.

After dinner and a bath, the tension gone, I went downstairs to participate in the Italian version of Trivial Pursuit, forming a team with the decidedly handsome and attractive Marco. Every time our turn came to toss the dice, we landed either a one or a six – regardless of which one of us did the tossing. It was unbelievable. With his usual dry humour, he shrugged:

– With me, it's always all or nothing. This is my disease.

I caused roars of laughter with my answer to the question, in Italian I might emphasize: 'Which is the oldest European *colonia*, still existing, in South America?'

Marco having not a clue, I confidently exclaimed:

– 4711 !

It is indeed the oldest eau de cologne in existence and its sales were booming in transatlantic countries.

– New Guinea, you dummy! The question referred to a political colony, not a perfume!

The answer to another question provided an enlightening piece of information: 'What do humans need repeatedly every day, called *polydipsia*?'

Nobody had the faintest idea. Yawning? Belching? No! 'Drinking'!

How could we have missed out on that one? Gilda and I exchanged merry glances. Even Gianni grinned.

Most of us went to the smoking salon afterwards. There sat a radiant Raquel.

– I've found a new flat at last! she exulted. Blinking at me she added:

– For singles only!

This calling for a major celebration, we invited each other to lavish rounds of decaffeinated Coca-Cola.

Even Reni, whom I have found a bit of a nuisance, turned out to be a sweet person. I always wondered how her hairdo could be so impeccable day after day. It's a wig. She has just completed an extremely intense chemotherapy which she might have to resume in a few months. It has drained her morale and body. But the lab results are encouraging, so there are grounds for much hope.

On my way upstairs, I caught a glimpse of Iñaki, the astrophysicist, and Giuseppe, the 'Music Monk', playing chess. It sort of comforted me, the way things do when they fall into place. Finally, I went to bed in high spirits, later than usual since I am no longer given infusions. I slept well, blissfully unsuspecting of what the morning's news would bring.

Tuesday

12 June

At about nine I heard someone calling my name from the garden. It was Marco. He gestured me to come down. Unshaved, with haunted eyes, looking utterly scared and dithered, his aspect indicated something sinister had happened. It had.

In the middle of the night, when a nurse had checked on all patients in the 'closed section', she found Kiki, the pretty twenty-five-year-old who had been psychotically enslaved by a sect and self-mutilated herself, in a pool of blood. She must have smuggled one of the crystal ashtrays scattered about in our 'section' into her room (neither glass nor metal items, nor even coins, are allowed over there), probably wrapped it in a towel to mute the noise as she broke it, then cut herself, slashing some veins. An ambulance arrived at once. Marco, hearing a car engine, had the darkest premonition and banged on his door until they let him out. He's a good friend of Kiki's.

She is now in the cantonal hospital, hovering between life and death, having presumably already undergone hours of surgery.

Marco asked me to call and tell Tonia. I had a feeling this was not a good idea.

– Why don't you take a shower and meet me here in half an hour?

– Okay.

Mercifully, I found who I was looking for. Dottore M was naturally abreast of events. I told him about Marco's request and my qualms regarding it.

– Tonia is the last person who should know.

He closed the door to his office behind me as I stepped inside.

– As you know, I am under a strict oath never to talk about

patients. Yet I will tell you this much: Kiki's attachment to Tonia worried me. She followed her everywhere, started dressing like her, etcetera. Tonia became her buoy and spiritual guide. Having experienced what she did, she is addicted to relationships based on obedience and devotion. On the other hand, Tonia was so kind and caring that I didn't dare interfere. My guess is that Tonia's departure produced the pain which triggered Kiki's desperate action last night. Now: Tonia being much more vulnerable than she seems, I entreat you *not* to call her. When we know the outcome of the operation, and should it be positive, I will do so myself. Should it be negative, I will leave it. Tonia has to readapt to her life and work. There is a danger she will feel responsible to a certain degree, and this must be avoided at all costs. May I count on you?

– You can, *dottore*.

On the threshold of his office he said:

– Incidentally, we had a meeting of the clinic's staff last night. I'm glad you felt left in peace, but you were under close scrutiny. Other than the fact that you smoke in your room instead of stepping out on the balcony to do so, for which I should chide you, I have rarely heard such a concert of compliments about your manners, consideration, making your bed knowing you don't have to and, not least, your vitality.

Wonderful, but Kiki's 'accident' made everything else pale into insignificance.

– Gilda and I are going downtown at ten. She wants to go to the Villa Favorita, I need leg-waxing and, *à propos* your kind staff, must pick up something. May Marco please come with us? I pleaded.

– No, he flatly answered. Rules are rules, and in the 'closed section' even less flexible.

– But he doesn't have an alcohol problem! What could go wrong? It might prevent him from sinking into one of his bouts of depression . . .

The doctor's refusal remained adamant.

– You can, however, convey good news: he will be transferred to the room you vacate on Thursday. But again – and please make that quite clear to Marco too: not a word, not a hint, not an intimation regarding last night's . . . incident. The fewer patients who know, the better.

I went out to transmit both messages. Some colour returned to Marco's face.

In Lugano's old town, it was market day, and a sunny one.

In my approximate Italian, I chatted with the refreshingly cheerful beautician. As I paid, she asked where I was staying.

– In a clinic, actually.

– Oh? Which one?

When I told her the name, she goggled.

– What are *you* doing there?

Casting furtive glances around, I whispered in a conspiratorial tone:

– I'm a polydipsic.

The poor girl gaped in puzzled alarm. That put an abrupt stop to further questioning.

I collected the two bouquets and found a toyshop where I bought a small Formula One car for Freddy. He had lost his cherished grandfather last week, Thursday was his birthday, and although he is a pain in the neck (whenever possible, he tries to kiss me), he is gentle behind the sort of appearance Tonia would appreciate, and nice the way some people are with an IQ below zero. His only interests seem to pertain to motor sports.

Gilda and I met again in a café on the main square. For the first time in a long while, I felt the itch of desire for some wine. It waned fast. When I showed Gilda the modest present, she told me that Freddy had had a catastrophic motorbike accident two years ago. He was pieced together surgically, but lost his memory and his speech faculty. He had to be taught Italian as in a kinder-garten. Among the reasons he is kept in the clinic – other than feelings of terror of his father – is his passion for all speedy things on wheels. Apparently, he still isn't fit to drive, and it is feared this is the first thing he'd do given a chance.

That made me once again reflect on warped judgements. I exchanged the racing car for a miniature tennis-match repro-duction. As an afterthought, I also bought a little wax piano for the 'Music Monk'.

At one we were back. No Marco in sight . . . The nurse had kept lunch warm for us. Then Gilda went to bed for a siesta: I had woken her up at 'dawn', shortly before nine. The 'music (caco-phony) therapy' was cancelled – much to my regret, for I had been looking forward to seeing Jacques again. He was ill. So instead, I started reading quite a good mystery novella

At six, Dottore G, the psychologist, and I met as we had agreed to discuss the results of both the tests, the Rorschach and the MMPI (standing for the Minnesota Multiphasic Personality Inventory). I was very curious.

The interminable list of questions you answer by putting a cross in yes or no boxes is entered into a computer, which then classifies them under such rubrics as hypomania, paranoia, depression, suicidal impulses, sociability, affectivity and sexuality. I will make a short story (he stayed twenty minutes at the most) even shorter.

Dottore G announced he would only stress the most pre-dominant personality traits:

– Persecution phobia.

(*What? I never felt persecuted, or paranoiac, in my entire life.*)

– Excessive mistrust of others.

(*I'm the most gullible, trusting person, have been told so and made fun of because of it over and again, and besides, have experienced the consequences first hand . . .*)

– Have a strong tendency to depression.

(*No kidding. Who doesn't around here?*)

– Lack of self-esteem.

(*Dixit. But neither am I over-burdened by an inferiority complex. It's not so much me I lack esteem for; it's for my lack of achievement – in particular, not having been able to publish anything but scattered articles so far.*)

– Trouble with sociability and communication with others.

(*Has the doctor mixed up his files?*)

– No self-confidence.

(*Nearer the truth. But why? No explanation.*)

– Mismanagement of anger.

(*No management at all, after too many drinks.*)

– Obsessive guilt feelings.

(*Bingo!*)

– Suicidal thoughts under the influence of excessive alcohol, when in psychological pain.

(*Right, but pain must be excruciating and extremely sentimental.*)

– *Insoma*, said Dottore G: (a) no more drinking until you can control your intake, which will require months or years, and never when in pain, because of the danger. (b) You perceive the future like an avalanche rolling towards you with increased acceleration, while standing petrified, naked and unprotected.

(*Wrong again. I often find time too static and life too repetitive. Rather than being afraid, I am impatient for things to get moving, to become more challenging, in short, for change.*)

He then proceeded to comment on the Rorschach also called 'the inkblot' test:

– Early relationships mould our future behaviour, and the earliest is with one's parents.

(*A scoop.*)

– I will comment on Image Four first: you saw a giant bird, with a predatory face, and were visibly put off. Well: it corresponds to the father figure and by extension to the masculine gender. My hypothesis: you feel threatened and helpless, scared and insecure in your relationship with your father – and with men in general.

– What was the mother figure? I asked icily.

– I was coming to that. Image Seven. The one in which you saw twins, the symbol of symmetry, similarity and harmony, still

floating in the womb, the epitome of protectiveness and warmth.
(*This was turning into a dubious joke.*)

– *Dottore*, I interrupted, we have a problem here. Either I need a lobotomy or the images were transposed. The case is the *exact opposite* of what you have described. What you say about my father is vaguely true regarding my perception of my mother and vice versa. May I add that my father *is* a twin, and that his sister was like a surrogate mother to me? Other than that, I have done much man-hopping in my life because the masculine gender, as you put it, gave me the sympathy, the feelings of security, *insoma*, the – more or less ephemeral – harmony I so desperately long for. No threats, no regrets. As a matter of fact, the one who has most hurt my feelings spent nine hours driving me here and back to Zurich, and the one who most hurt my pride is having lunch with me with next Friday. The two men who most matter in my life, my father and my husband, never caused me the slightest harm. Who do you think financed my being here?

Dottore G looked most uncomfortable. Just as well he wasn't his own patient, I mused; or was he?

– What about the meaning of the picture I described as this American spy-plane, the Stealth, surrounded by dark clouds, as I thought, preceded and followed by red blots I interpreted as fire?

– Ah, said the doctor, rubbing his hands, very interesting. That was Image Twelve: the phallus. My hypothesis is that sex, since men are threatening – (*was he deaf, or didn't he believe a word?*) – is to you a source of conflict, confrontation, yes indeed, practically of war.

At this point I had to make a superhuman effort to keep a straight face. I hoped the man didn't gamble. At the same time, annoyance was encroaching. What a waste of time and money!

Conclusion or delusion: either this is a load of crap, or I am so barmy I belong in the 'closed section' – where body-search has been reintroduced today, for reasons mysterious to many, though sadly not to me.

He had told me nothing of which I was not either already

acutely aware or else knew to be wrong. Before he left Dottore G added:

– I forgot to mention another striking feature of your personality according to the MMPI: your logical, almost mathematical mind.

This was too much. I burst out laughing. Why bother to tell this genius that I have the greatest trouble calculating a simple percentage, and that, my logic being extremely feminine, it is an understatement to describe it as whimsical?

He left with a concerned expression on his face. He will certainly conclude I am in denial regarding my true fucked-up self.

Dinner arrived. It looked so inedible that I went to the supermarket across the road to buy vast amounts of cheese and a baguette. To be able to cross the street without needing to ask permission or take an alcohol test on coming back was one of these small treats that make you realize that freedom is exactly that: small steps, no mistrust or censorship.

The daily thunderstorm, around five o'clock, had passed and gone, and I prayed it would not break out on Thursday. My plane to Geneva leaves at six p.m., and it being a twin-propeller cuckoo, that would be none to pleasant. (Hinting at its modernity and comfort, Lucca had renamed Fly Baboo 'Fly Bamboo'.)

In the smoking salon, I met Raff, my taciturn next-balcony neighbour, to whom Dottore G had paid a visit before coming to see me.

– How did the conversation go? I asked with feigned nonchalance.

Though he is one of the more phlegmatic people around, Raff gazed at me in a stupor before jumping to his feet.

– Conversation? You joking? At first I thought he must have mixed his files up; then I was amused; in the end I was enraged.

– You don't say.

He started pacing the salon. We were alone.

– First he tells me I have memory-shortage problems. It's the one problem I don't have. My memory is elephantine, always has been – which might be a problem, actually. Then he claims I cannot relate to my son. We work together, we live together, and there has never been the remotest strain between us. Remember the white sort of triangle? I couldn't help but see a body covered by a sheet after a lethal car crash. His preposterous conclusion had something to do with my regarding sexual intercourse as an accident and wishing to have my dick cut off. *Jeeeeesus!* When he started on about some 'hypothesis' over my dreading the implications of my parents' old age, i.e. getting tanked to duck responsibility, I threw the man out. My mother died while giving birth to me, my father shortly thereafter. That charlatan should be defrocked!

I could no longer repress my hilarity. Raff never asked what I had thought or why I laughed. He couldn't have cared less. He sank back into the sofa and his Olympian calm. He is one of these people with whom you could cross an ocean on a small boat and know no better on arrival than when you raised anchor.

I returned to my room and wrote these pages. The truth is that I sizzled with disappointment.

I often feel confronted with 'a riddle wrapped in a mystery inside an enigma' (as Churchill described the Russians) when attempting to understand the mechanisms of my mind or certain recurrent behaviour patterns. One would expect such lengthy tests to provide explanations, or elucidations, to questions with which one struggles to no avail. Dottore G's insipid psychobabble and platitudes had provided nothing but bewilderment.

On the bedside table, I caught sight of a small envelope: 'Dear countess, K out of danger. Sleep well. Dr M.' (He austerely refuses to call me by my first name.)

That made me happy. Yet, once in bed, I wondered: was Kiki relieved? She had committed her deed dead sober (sorry for the bad pun), and her carefully monitored medication was based on antidepressants and sedatives. She had planned her scheme, and waited for what she considered an appropriate time of night.

There must have been a lot more to it than Tonia's absence. She was due to go home soon, provided she came back in three weeks.

It reminded me of the laconic note the even younger daughter of a famous TV French news commentator left before killing herself: *'Je n'aime pas la vie'* – 'I do not like life.' Presumably to exorcize his pain, her father wrote a book about it, which I didn't wish to read, but soon might, after all.

Wednesday

There was no way I could fall asleep. At two in the morning I rang for the nurse and was given half a pill. She was the Cerebus type who stares at you. In case you cut the half-pill into a quarter? Jesus. At seven-thirty I was in an irascible mood. I had slept little and badly. The Kiki story, the rubbish I had listened to at astronomical cost (as I suspected and the bill would confirm) had me on edge.

I read most of what I had written since my arrival and wasn't impressed. In fact, it upset me further. Setting oneself awesome standards leads to disillusion: hadn't I heard enough of that recently?

Dottore M materialized before lunch. I had a few words with him, not too carefully minced. Basically, I told him that the art therapist was more lucid than Dottore G with his computers and consorts. I cited the example of the Stealth shape, making it quite clear it was a random case.

– Rather than a phallus, what it revealed to me was a threatening, pyramidal structure. My head is cluttered with them, my feelings very ambivalent in that respect.

– What do you mean?

– Everything, of course, I retorted with insolent languor.

– Please elaborate.

– Infancy and family? A triangle. My emotional life, so far? More often than not, also a triangle. My geographical situation? Considering travels, another triangle: Munich, Palma and 'elsewheres'. My personality? A triangle again, being as emotional as cerebral, and as cerebral as irrational. Sexually, as the *dottoressa* will have gathered from my fantasies, a fifth triangle.

– Why do you say feel ambivalent about it? he asked, looking concerned, but about something else.

– Because on the one hand I love triangular situations – sometimes even consciously prefer and create them – and on the other hand they tear me apart. That's why.

I was becoming bored by my own voice again, with the nagging feeling that the duet lacked a supporting voice. Perhaps I also wrote too much. Dottore M's beeper started shrieking. Hopefully not another emergency. He leapt to his feet.

– Tomorrow we will meet in my office with Dottoressa D and have a final talk. You do not yet realize how noticeable your improvements are. As your doctor, I feel gratified.

– Thank you for last night's note.

– *A domani, contessa.*

This title-tic got on my nerves, not only because I am used to being called Aleana, but also because it maintained the distance he insisted upon, and which I had hoped to overbridge.

I needed a coffee, decaffeinated or not. It was crowded downstairs as the skies were pouring with diluvian rain. Chasing away my foul mood, I noticed that Marco was having a spirited conversion with Freddy.

– Good news?

– Yes. I talked to the hospital where Kiki is, and they seem optimistic. Then I spoke to my wife. She's finally agreed to a legal separation.

– Does Tonia know?

His smile answered my question.

– She's coming next Sunday. She said she sleeps a lot.

– Lucky her.

I left them to their political talk and spent the rest of the day in my room. In protest at the fact that the *atelier* is charged as an extra, as I was told only today, I boycotted it this once. Gianni, devoted to his job, came to see me and said he would arrange for my name not to appear on the list. I told him I would rather join in on the Trivial Pursuit after dinner.

– Shame. Your enthusiasm is infectious.

Before dinner I made some superfluous calls. I needed to talk, not about myself for a change, but about, no matter what. The foul mood had turned into mixed feelings . . . about everything. As I stepped out of the phone booth, an American woman, already outrageously silicone-scaffolded, was checking in for another kind of uplifting. She was escorted by an Italian beau who, although of Tarzanesque proportions, was heaving her two huge Vuitton suitcases with visible difficulty. The pair made a caricature of the forever-blonde, forever-young and very vulgar Texan socialite with her Latin gigolo.

– Kick the stuff in a corner, Micky Mouse, she squeaked. Where's that Doctor M fella? Where's everybody in this joint, for J. F. Christ's sake?

It was half past seven and reception is deserted around then.

– Tell ya what, kid, go fetch somebody, else I'm outta here, she drawled in that husky but shrill voice of hers.

One of the girls from admissions stepped into the hall.

– Where the helluva you been, doll? the Texan exclaimed with irritation.

– *Scusi?*

– Dunno understand these folks. Micmoooo, talk to that gal!

The beau did as he was told. It turned out she was to be a patient in the closed section. She had probably attempted murder after suicide, or the other way round.

– You kiddin'me? she burst out haughtily, by now shaking with wrath, having been told that smoking was forbidden except in the salon or outside. If I can't smoke in Europe, ain't I gonna stay in the US of A or go to China, goddammit? Not in this dump a gaol, for F's sake.

Dottore M emerged from his office.

– *Benvenutta, signora.*

– What?

– Welcome.

– Thanks, she crooned, suddenly a pussycat. (Poor 'Micky Mouse'.)

I observed the scene in a semi-detached way, but internally was hooting with laughter, especially when she announced:

– Tell ya what, doc, I'm off for a nap before dinner, see, getting unpacked and all that jazz.

When her gigolo translated that dinner time was over and the kitchen closed, she yelled and gesticulated hysterically.

– Waddya saying? You goddam clinic whatchacallit creeps! Bet the food's lousy anyway! . . . You'll never see an oil barrel again if I dunno get dinner, *now*! You goddam clinic whatchercallit creeps! Who needs you anyway? I hate all of you!

She had turned into a wild-eyed shrew within seconds. The harangue went on and on. Dottore M's conciliatory laugh was about as spontaneous as an alarm clock's buzzer, but it had her giggling convulsively all of a sudden. I felt sure this wasn't the woman's first time in a clinic, and wondered how long it would take before some fat cigar-puffing lawyer came to bail her out. Her going ballistic provoked high-pitched giggles from Toy-Boy. There was something grotesquely pathetic about it all. Last thing I heard was her shrieking:

– Fun-nee, it's so fun-neeee, Capreee, sey fineeeee . . . (Poor nurses.)

Trudging up the stairs, heavy-hearted again, I crossed paths with the 'Music Monk' on his way down. He signalled me to wait. When he returned, he gave me a hand-written sheet of music. It appeared to be, and probably was, a musical poem; at the bottom, his name and mine in green ink in hieroglyphs, or so it was made to look. He mimed taking off a hat and bowed. I shall never forget his smile: it transmitted more kindness, modesty and melancholy than can be put into words, or notes. Then he hummed something, to himself only.

The Trivial Pursuit game was relaxing, as its name suggests.

Last Day

Thursday, 14 June

In a happy way I was sad to pack. After a night's deep sleep, without any Trittico – removing the Trazadone-based pill from underneath my tongue on the nurse's departure had been a conclusive experiment – I felt well, rested and confident. Even though Dottore M had warned me on occasion that the beneficiary effects of these two weeks would be delayed, I interpreted my undisturbed sleep as a promising omen.

There were visible signs of recovery too: the rings under my eyes had disappeared, and I no longer lamented finding my comb full of hair after every time I washed it. My digestion wasn't being disrupted by nervous diarrhoea, the effects of which showed on my skin.

Having lived in a reduced space for two weeks, I had Scotch-taped all sorts of things to the wall: the weekly programme, as printed out by the clinic; two letters that mean a lot to me; ideas to include in this diary; the map of Lugano, and so on. Without them, the room seemed stripped of its soul. Before embarking on a farewell tour, I realized once more that everyone I had met during my stay was uniquely attaching. 'Out there', addicted people recognize and attract each other, drawn by a perverse magnet. 'In here', there are no clandestine bonds; instead, solidarity reigns supreme, the matching piece to naked sincerity.

My favourite nurse, appropriately called Angelina, came in to take a last blood test.

– I'd rather wait until I'm back in Spain, I argued, while thinking: no way!

She understood and smiled. I had left the accountant a note saying: 'A thousand thanks, multiplied by ten!'

You might think that two weeks on an alcohol- and salt-free diet would make you loose a few pounds, but it doesn't. Presumably the explanation is the massive doses of vitamins and minerals, combined with a lack of exercise.

As summoned, I entered the reunion room at twelve sharp. There sat Dottore M, Dottoressa D and, thankfully, *not* Dottore G with a last-minute psychological test of his own concoction.

The *dottoressa* spoke first:

– As you know, I have tried to explore your affective background and perceptions. First, permit me to say that you should be closer to your husband, and I do not only mean in space or time but also in communication. Most men never answer unasked questions. You seem to lament the fact that he talks so reluctantly about his own problems, thoughts or feelings. I suggest you ask more questions.

She consulted her notes.

– As to the subject of your mother – not a pleasant one, I know – my impression is the following. Remember how you mentioned having robbed her of the joys of being a grandmother? From *her* emotional point of view, Aleana, you did much worse. You robbed her of her need to be needed.

Dottoressa D let that sink in before she resumed:

– Now, our patient not being your mother but you, it is your point of view that matters; and from that angle, she is a highly toxic person. I will not emit opinions regarding her relationships with others.

She smiled warmly, hinting that she personally knew what she was talking about.

– You are a vital person. Do not let your energy be watered down, wasted or filtered out by your mother, nor by any other toxic. You won't change them. Don't bear the brunt of their bitterness – their common denominator *being* frustration. Avoid them.

– They aren't always easy to recognize, at least not soon enough . . .

– Right. But I'll enumerate a few characteristics shared by

people who undermine others, invading their mind, causing emotional stress, sadness and anger. To begin with: some words heal; others harm. Toxics are good at manipulating them. Endowed with instinctive and sophisticated radars, they spot where it most hurts. Low self-esteem is, in their case, centrifuged into dominance. They know better, always have done, fighting alone in a hostile world that undervalues them. Nothing is ever absolutely right when it's out of their control. Constantly dissatisfied, critical of all with the manic exception of themselves, toxics are perfectionists to a neurotic degree in most situations. They need to mimic feeling and feel their best when feeling low – as was the case with your mother at the Geneva dinner party. Being the perfect hostess is equally of crucial importance to her. Weakness just isn't acceptable.

She drank two glasses of water. Her turn! I tried to scribble down what she said, but she was a fast talker when she got going.

– Toxics are busy-bees. They seek constant occupation and a permanent audience – the need to be needed. They furnish time by being disorganized and getting priorities mixed up. As a consequence, most of them are chronically late. Their unpunctuality, however, has a specific intention. It's one of the toxic's manoeuvres to assert: 'People can wait. I'm worth it.' Compliments are what *they* are addicted to, or dependent on, to feel alive. If need be, they'll struggle ferociously for it, discarding their principles and using convoluted tricks. The most classic and recurrent of these? Managing not to do what they want, thereby shifting the blame for their dissatisfaction on to others.

One image irrepressibly sprang to my mind. Dottoressa D had sketched a pretty accurate identikit portrait for Hugo. Hugo? Well . . . he certainly had been toxic for me sixteen years ago, and on an atomic scale. He no longer was, but you can divorce from a man, not from a parent.

– All you just said could describe a lot of people . . .

– Maybe. What's for sure is that *the one thing you can rely on is that they cannot be trusted*. They are masterly at extracting intimate confessions, at patting and flattering, but it's mainly to feel they're at the wheel and let third parties know that they, and *only they*, have been told this or that – which they usually can't refrain from relaying. Unfriendly takeovers of others' lives are frequent. The feeling of self-importance is cardinal to their personality, as toxics intoxicate themselves by sheer force of character, she sighed.

Again, her formulas brought home all-too-familiar flashbacks. Having been so reserved during our talks, she now seemed inexhaustible. We must have shared more than superficial experiences, for she resumed vehemently:

– Toxics are their own worst enemies; spend much energy eschewing self-confrontation but are not inclined to substance abuse, lest it diminish their power – over you, in this instance. Do keep your distance.

– I can't avoid my own mother for the rest of both our lives . . . In two months, she turns eighty, and . . .

– Seeing her on social occasions is fine, so long as you remember to stay in the background: leave her the limelight. But alone with her, or in small gatherings, especially if at *her* home where she's 'the boss', I insist you avoid it, Aleana. To you, and only you, she is even more poisonous than alcohol, being a weighty cause of your drinking. Her despising those who drink to hide what alcohol actually reveals, i.e. weakness, is a witch-hunt: it scares her. At the same time it has probably incited you to go for it, as a way of backing away from her. But okay, let's leave it at that.

She sighed again, suddenly reminding me of school teachers who wish they could have done more after their students graduate, probably never to return or even keep in touch. That was a thought that had always moved me no end.

– I also advise you to spurn sad books, tragic films, in short, to turn away from all upsetting situations that can possibly be steered clear of, at least in the months to come. Dodging a danger isn't necessarily cowardice.

– Many months, interrupted Dottore M. with emphasis, signalling he wanted to move on. It is good that you feel confident, contessa. However, I cannot stress enough how prudent you must learn to become. *Do not think you are strong, because you are not.* You are fragile, and giving up alcohol is especially difficult when coupled with depressiveness. People with only one of the two problems have less trouble. You have inherited a brain structure which is, in essence, receptive to high amounts of serotonin; this, combined with the imbalance of oestrogen caused by the menopause, will make you subject to cravings. My colleague has addressed the precautions you must take affectively. Let me concentrate on the more practical aspects of abstinence. To begin with: you have no choice but the zero option.

I didn't like hearing it, since I also knew the answer to, 'For how long?' Same as with cigarettes, for one incapable of moderation. 'It's all or nothing,' Marco would have sniggered.

– What my colleague said about toxic persons is equally true of toxic substances. The other day you told me you had an alcohol-free beer. Careful: it reactivates the wrong circuits. It's a bit like campaigning against fur coats and wearing cashmere – in other words, cheating. It prolongs your 'trip'.

Seeing my sad grimace, he shrugged.

– I know. But you understood my point. More importantly: learn to identify people, times and places that are perilous. Cravings last between five and ten minutes, no more: that's the good news. The bad news is that if you cannot, during that time, hold on to someone for support, or concentrate on something else, the relapse risk is multiplied. Are there AA groups where you live?

– Drinking being a national sport in Spain, they're all over the place. But sitting around with strangers and telling the same story over and over . . .

– You did it here, and enjoyed it.

– Oh?

– Did you wonder why we haven't introduced group therapy? In a loose form, that's exactly what we do. Letting our patients wander around the garden, organizing games, insisting on your participation in art or music groups (not composed at random, in parenthesis), is this clinic's form of group therapy. By talking and listening to others, albeit at a time and place of your choice, patients unconsciously form groups to undergo therapy within them.

He was absolutely right, come to think of it. We had all exchanged and shared life stories, fears, experiences and dreams. Explaining our opportunities and motives, we became 'partners in crime'.

– To come to the subject of depression: constant morning exhaustion is its indisputable symptom. A psychologically healthy person gets going, recovers fast even if lacking a few hours' sleep or having a hangover. Your depression is not, by any means, chronic, let alone manic, but it is there and diagnosed – in its incubate stage. You have tackled the collaterals of menopause in the worst of ways. Rather than resorting to benzodiazepines, you should have taken antidepressants from the very beginning of your insomnias.

Dottore M knew perfectly well that it had been the neurologist I consulted who had prescribed those tranquillizers, Trankimaztin or Bikalm. Okay, he also knew that I had toyed with various variations on this theme, in the idiotic belief it would prevent habituation to any. Orfidal, Remestan, Lexomil, Stilnox, you name it: nowadays even a vet examining your canary bird prescribes you the stuff if you charm him into compassion, the chances being he is on some drug or other too.

– The ten-milligram Cipralex we have given you do not cause dependency, it's a low dosage, but you may have to take them for the rest of your life.

– *For the rest of my life?*

– Yes, *cara*.

It was a shock, and one that hit me hard. Noting this, Dottore M explained:

– Depressed subjects cannot drive, organize themselves or even watch television. Images get blurred; sounds and images don't synchronize and can no longer be deciphered. This has never been so in your case. Depression-*prone* subjects skate on thin ice, which may, at the slightest crack, tumble them into the pathological state. The danger hovers above their lives for as long as they live. Prevention is better than cure. First thing to do back home: a blood test checking your hormonal state. As for the next few months: always, I repeat, always *do* something: write, clean your cupboards, do sports, whatever. *Always* be prepared to confront cravings. I would not expect you to become a hermit. Since you don't like sweet soft drinks, *always* take V8, Tonic Schweppes or, *va bene*, a non-alcoholic beer with you when invited to friends' houses. Same thing on beaches or boats; there are very practical thermo-bags nowadays.

Looking at me with what seemed sincere affection, he added:

– Finally, *never* hesitate to call us. If we're not here, there'll be another doctor who will retrieve your file from the computer within minutes and know how to help if need be. The less expensive alternative is finding a support group in Palma. My advice: find an NA rather than an AA structure.

– What's that?

– Narcotics Anonymous. They are usually composed of more interesting people, I must admit, but are rather selective and seclusive. If they ask you why you prefer NA, say that in abusing alcohol and tranquillizers, you fabricated a drug within your organism.

Great. He seemed to deliberate whether or not to add something more:

– Regarding expenses: I have heard that you found our bill on the high side. If you come back – and I *strongly* recommend you do in November to stabilize your recovery, be it only for ten days, since most relapses occur after five months' abstinence (*why not three or seven, search me: it's a statistic*) the treatments will be far less costly: no Phlebo, no psychological tests, less medication. We will all be glad to welcome you again. *Veramente*.

Dottore M and I shook hands effusively. The *dottoressa* and I hugged and she said:

– If I had your sex-appeal, I would devour life with fervour, she added in a feverish whisper.

What was the matter with her, I could not help wondering, as her hand touched my breast instead of my shoulder? A dike shrink would have given a giddy dimension to the *gran finale*.

– Thank you both so infinitely much. It was lovely here.

Though I meant it, the one thing I wanted right then was to get the hell out of this 'paradise'.

Marco and I had agreed to go for a last walk in the garden. It seemed important, to us both I think. We had brushed the surfaces and the epidermis of our minds and sensitivities in such a cautious way that bluntness had been tacitly ruled out. He started telling me about a long conversation his wife, his consultant doctor and he had conducted earlier, and how relieved he felt they had reached an accord on separation. His wife, Fiori, had a totally different outlook from his on lifestyles, their daughter's education and practically all else. One really wonders. Many believe they'll be able to change their partner. Marco sighed:

– The mere desire to change somebody one loves is a fallacious premise.

I would have wished to hold Marco in my arms, as a sister can but a friend can't. Why is this so?

What intrigued me, but I had not dared address before, was how such an active, lucid and intelligent person could have believed, for a while, that he was God's illegitimate son. (This being said, he had been at the clinic a whole month before my arrival. That he looked as perfectly normal, contented and well as most of the others was hardly surprising under treatment. It was the way we had all behaved previously that made the mind boggle.)

Marco explained what the manic state *really* implies: not necessarily frantic agitation and euphoria, as I had thought. It starts in a subtle way: signs, signals and sensory symptoms. He had begun to smell incense, to hear voices, and had been alarmed when the third stage – visual hallucinations – set in. This third stage is precisely the one that, once overstepped, leads into the inferno of schizophrenia. As a child he had been baptized by a very renowned cardinal, the Pope's cousin no less. His lunatic mother was staunchly devout, and his cousin, following similar mental delusions, had become a priest after hitherto being one of Italy's most successful entrepreneurs. In the manic state, physical endurance is multiplied manifold. He hardly needed sleep and could tackle the most exacting tasks. Cocaine helped.

Marco talked with a forlorn self-derision. He was another to confess he was terrified of returning to the outside world, but the only one who quite grimly predicted that once he was there he would certainly relapse into his former condition; it would only be a question of time. When I didn't react, he looked disappointed. I guess he mistook my silence for disbelief, which unfortunately it wasn't.

The time had come for us to go to art therapy, which was scheduled to end ten minutes before the taxi to the airport was due to arrive for me.

Again, talent and interpretations alike were stunning. Iñaki, the Basque astrophysicist, painted within an hour another picture one would have liked to frame. From left to right across an A3 sheet, above a dark-blue undulating sea occupying more than a third of the bottom space, it represented two atmospheres: the sky in which shone a sun with long, intensely green and yellow rays. Another third of the sky was cloudy and rainy. On a steep, vertical promontory, or a cliff, sat Iñaki. Above him, a zero and the symbol of infinity, ∞, its second oval open where it overlapped the edge of the sheet. Underneath, lashing at the rocks, a high, sprinkling wave rebounding to the surface.

The sea was divided by a yellow, vertical line. Below the sun was a calmer, less nuanced surface and mass; beneath the rain, descending from the yellow line which bisected the sea, was an irregular, descending curve, also yellow.

Iñaki explained:

– This is a place I know, where I used sit for hours. Opposite is a small harbour. I liked it, rain or shine. Underneath the clouds there is more turmoil in the sea. The curve is somewhat seismic. I drew it because the big bang that engendered the universe was asymmetric, thereby to show that initial imperfection isn't necessarily negative.

– Well, observed the therapist, Dottoressa Beatrix, dreamily . . . as you did last week, you represent a dual, binary world. Here again: a sharp division between tranquillity and turmoil. This time, though, you are in it – as a spectator, one who questions the meaning of it all. This is a step forward. You probably know Einstein's words: the formulation of a problem is more important than its solving? Still at the edge of it, you nevertheless are *in there*.

Marco's painting was a vast confusion of geometrical forms and shapes, in gravity-free space, like the aftermath of an explosion. Yet again, the colours were pastel. It didn't suggest an incandescent or loud explosion. In the middle: the same dark, purple cube, devoid of window or door. Now, however, drawn with spaced lines, tentative openings were appearing. Some fresh air was being allowed in. He commented:

– This is a reaction to Fiori mentally accepting diverging perspectives. Life will change. I can finally move to Crans-Montana, after we sort out how we divide up things and responsibilities. It's rather confusing at this point.

– What you will also have to decide, Marco, emphasized Dottoressa Beatrix, is which facets of your personality you must give up to leave behind, which you must treasure and enhance. The more you can relinquish and leave behind, the more space you will have for the future you.

Her advice awoke deep resonances in me.

– One more thing: where's your little daughter?

– With her mother, leading a so-called normal life.

– And where are you?

– Inside. Invisible.

From his expression, we all felt he would go no further. He was in pain.

The therapist turned to my collage.

– Why did you sign with a name other than your real one?

– Because it's a pen name and, by extension, one that I spontaneously used in another art form.

– Fair enough. Let's come back to the triangles.

I repeated more or less what I had said to Dottore M.

– Your choice of two predominant colours that aren't often combined, pink and yellow, is arresting. I won't get into the subtleties of Aura-Soma or colour psychology. Only colour symbolism is of relevance here. Yellow and pink are combined shades with positive connotations but only a few common denominators: ambiguity is the one that I must stress. Femininity in both cases is tinged with ambivalence, and in the case of pink, associated with bisexuality (there she looked me straight in the eye) when in the form of a triangle.

The others examined me with renewed interest. This provoked an urge to laugh. Ask Dottoressa D, I thought, as it bubbled up. My laughter turned out to be infectious, but left the therapist unfazed.

– Yellow, the obvious symbol of sunlight and air, is in Egypt the colour of mourning and was during the Middle Ages used to depict the devil. In astrology it is associated with the sign of Taurus.

What could I say? Nothing seemed best. I was born at the very beginning of May.

– You chose, in the left upper angle and the right bottom one, two photographs representing gaiety and grace. The text you affixed to these images contradicts, or perhaps challenges them in your mind: 'Conditional freedom.' 'A team game.' 'Without scalpels or injections.'

I had juxtaposed these captions around a laughing, healthy girl and glued 'Defend your feet' diagonally to an alluring hand with pink gloves up to the elbow. So what? It seemed fun at the time.

– A welcoming gesture – while ready to run away? In the right upper angle and in the left bottom one are two photographs representing problems, and I venture to say personal ones. Above, the reaching out to another person of the opposite sex, with 'His psyche' and 'Her psyche' inserted in the gap the two pairs of hands are unable to bridge. Below, a *horizontal* bottle, associated with the words 'eternity', 'facility' and 'therapy'. Why?

– Well, alcohol turns things upside down, for a start. Also . . . I like the impact of words and the irony of associations. I like revealing contrasts and do suffer, as you said, from reaching out without getting as close as I hope to the other, of whatever sex. The two ballet dancers, on the other hand, and the wild horse, are full of movement, so . . . there's always some dynamic hope.

– I see.

Did she? And what, exactly? Much too intent on hidden signification as she was, I wondered if she could capture gratuitous irony.

– In the middle, the photograph, cut into a triangle – again! – a sailing boat, and underneath a quote from Gombrowicz: 'I am the centre of the world.' So are you. In front of the mirror, train yourself to say that the right attitude makes everything else fall into place. Underneath, a picture of the title page of his book called *Testament*.

– Boats and the sea are to me the symbols of freedom and . . .

– Escape?

– No. Of forgetting oneself – a form of escape; in fact, yes, but towards the horizon. Writing is an island.

– A solitary one? Explaining the smallness of the boat? Anything to do with your feeling 'quartered' between disillusion and faith? Isn't the word 'Testament' in contradiction with your sailing into the sunset?

Suspecting where she was leading me, I jumped off.

– A testament is a farewell letter, in no contradiction with moving on and going ahead. Haven't you explained that only minutes ago?

– Is it a contradiction?

– Hmm . . . The title you seem to give to your collage, in bold pink letters along the left corner, is 'The future is always pinker'. Is that what you feel?

– Yes.

– All right. Isn't that all a bit too complex for comfort?

– Comfort is not what I am heading for, I smiled blandly.

– Whatever. Before you leave for your personal Wishland, one last comment: some of your captions being glued perpendicularly or diagonally to the images means one must either turn the folio about or walk round it. Misunderstandings in relationships and blockages in communication are often caused by confused perspectives, or by an unwillingness to move and alter them. That might be worth a thought. Good luck.

After rushed goodbyes, I jumped into the waiting taxi.

Looking back at the ivy-hung pale-yellow façade, and at the two weeks I had spent within it, I felt breathless, but without the accelerated heartbeat that usually goes with breathlessness. It was strange. The usual thunderstorm was approaching.

I might have cried had my being simultaneously sad and happy, and my wearing mascara, not reminded me that I'm only a woman after all, and supposedly a stronger one.

I also thought of my writing. One always tells about endings, doesn't one? Parting from a loved one, severed relationships, heartbreaks, separations from family, exiles, leaving a part of one's self behind. Stories are about ruptures. I also mused that, while I certainly have the gene, I just as certainly do not have the germ for depression – the real one. Too many imperceptible things make me ineffably happy; they always have done and always will.

Finally, I resolved never to travel without Scotch tape.

The Two Stories

1

Double
or The Man who Most Wounded My heart

'And I said that it had never occurred to me that he'd rather be shooting hoops than in bed with me, and he said that, yes, in fact, sometimes he would prefer to play basketball, and that in terms of absolute value, sex and sports were equally meaningless to him, they were just two ways to have fun . . .

'At heart, I have always been a coper. I've mostly been able to walk around with my wounds safely hidden, and I've always stored up my deep depressive episodes for the weeks off when there was time to have an abbreviated version of a complete breakdown.'

Elizabeth Wurtzel, *Prozac Nation*

On the terrace of the Café du Flore, the get-together in the formerly bohemian Saint Germain des Près, the Sunday paper ritual seems paralysed in a freeze frame. The hazy heat of this August afternoon is oppressive.

A conversation at a nearby table shakes me out of my lethargy. The voices, albeit indistinct, ring a distant bell.

– I think I saw Aleana a while ago.

– Impossible . . .

After a pause the man's boyish voice resumes:

– How do you know? She disappeared. All else is speculation.

– Forget her.

– I can't.

– Why not?

– She needed me.

– Aleana had everything and more, don't you worry, snaps the elegant lady in her seventies.

Another leaden silence follows.

– Not really. She had very few things . . .

– . . . but everything twice, answers the woman sarcastically.

– True. I remember how puzzled I was when I first went to her flat. Two identical frames on the walls, both empty, in the entrance. No doors. In the drawing room, two identical sofas, two identical African masks, two identical mirrors, both smoked to the point of reflecting nothing but foggy emptiness . . .

– There might not have been much to see.

– I opened her cupboards while she fixed drinks, the young man continues. Every item of clothing was hanging in identical pairs, in two different colours. Two pairs of shoes, but those in the same colour, on the railings. Then the photographs. All of them represented twin-like couples . . . I suppose you've been there?

– Never. What for?

– Well. Aren't you her mother, after all?

In midst of the torrid heat, I shiver. If they spot me, not only am I missing, but lost.

– Why Aleana continues haunting you flabbergasts me. She intrigued people more than she attracted them. Especially men.

This is right. I was never reassuring. I leave traces. More often than not, scars.

– You don't understand, insists the young man. She always seemed on the run, or on guard, something like that . . . She inspired protectiveness.

– Come off it, interrupts the lady. Collectors are maniacs! Can't you see that the absence of mirrors, the empty frames and so forth reflected her denial of images, her inability to face facts, reality, let alone herself?

Distrusting my impulses, I don't move. Suddenly, the woman turns around, stares at me, screams, then leaps to her feet pointing a black dagger and shooting me with phosphorescently cobalt eyes. Simultaneously, my sight bounces off white walls.

*   *   *

– Calm down, whispers a ghostly shape with a moon-like face. My name is Christine. It's only an injection.

– A what?

– An injection, dear. You must have had a nightmare. That's quite frequent after heavy anaesthetics.

– Heavy what?

– A three-hour operation requires rest. The doctor will see you later.

Upright in the bed, I try to make sense of it all. Scrutinizing the penumbra, I realize this is indeed a hospital.

– What happened?

– An accident. Don't worry, it'll be all right.

– What kind of an accident?

The nurse patted me and was gone.

What am I doing there? Why is my left hand bandaged? Last thing I remember is taking a shower. Hugo was coming from Strasburg just for one night. Then? The doors were locked . . . Yes . . .

Fragments of the recent past surfaced in random sequence.

Victoria and I had quarrelled shortly after checking into the Park Hotel in Baden-Baden. This time it had not been about something trivial. She mocked my love for Hugo. Besides, I wanted her to move out of the flat we had been sharing in Paris for almost a year. It was mine, to start with, and what had begun as a casual friendship turned out too intense for me. At first, I had welcomed her presence. But Victoria prevented me from writing. She had become possessive, invading, and in the end tyrannical. I had no one but myself to blame for this kind of 'takeover'.

There was a telephone in our suite's bathroom. It rang. Hugo. He said he had not been able to leave earlier; he would be in

Baden-Baden as soon as possible but would have to leave first thing in the morning – sorry – so please, not to wait for dinner.

Since his voice sounded cheerful, so was I. The ordeal was over! He had sorted things out. Perhaps even been given the embassy he had coveted.

Victoria walked in, a bottle of vodka in her hand.

– I bet that was your phoney prince oozing with his flaky charm.

– That's right, I answered gaily.

– I bet he said he'd be late.

– Vic, you don't like him, I know, but let it be. He can't just jump into private planes as you do.

I first met Victoria shortly after returning from Rome where I had lived a summer of passion. Hugo was married. He was a diplomat. Our affair became rumoured and was likely to jeopardize both his marriage and his career. His father-in-law, an Italian tycoon, made that quite clear. Hugo nevertheless filed for a divorce. Then all hell broke loose. This meant I had to vanish, at least for as long as it would take to settle matters. The embassy in Madrid had been promised to him.

All just a question of time, hand on heart. Not much time either.

I adored Hugo. He was everything I respected and needed. A lucid dreamer, interested in people and in ideas. The kind of looks I like – black hair, aquamarine eyes – of which he seemed unaware. Attractively taciturn, he never sought to be the centre of attention.

It felt like first love to me. He felt the same, swearing that whereas some people fall in and out of infatuation throughout life, he was a man who would love but once and I was that true and only one. I believed him.

As for Victoria, the heiress of an indecent American fortune, she did whatever she pleased whenever she wanted. Victoria came from a WASP family where appearance was the essence and books were classified in alphabetical order. She had been brought up in the cult of power and its relentless pursuit.

I was born in a 'steel baron' clan, split by a notorious bankruptcy, where manners and culture eclipsed gold and glitter. Idleness was a facet of detachment. One of my cousins once offered my father a calculator that would do nothing but subtractions. My father laughed: 'Things could be worse.'

In any case, Victoria's family looked on the likes of us with a mixture of archaeological curiosity and blunt condescension, while mine was bemused by their parvenu ostentation. 'Better nouveau riche than never rich,' she would snicker.

By and large, a melancholic frivolity was something Victoria and I had in common – but little more. She acted tough as nails, I acted cool as a cucumber, but our smooth patinas hid very distinct cores. She was always on the offensive, I on the defensive. Vic inspired challenge and conquest, not tenderness. She felt like an orphan, having been emotionally 'betrayed', as she said, by a ruthless father and an alcoholic mother. I had a loving father and, on the whole, a disciplined if pharisee mother.

What we shared, other than camouflaged vulnerabilities, was a very similar sense of humour, and as one knows, laughter creates strong bonds. We also shared a love for books and collected rare editions.

As she stood next to me as I piled up my hair before stepping into the shower, I was once again struck by our resemblance in the mirror. She could have been the negative of a photograph of me: as dark as I was fair, her hair being short and mine long, her skin as tanned as mine was pale. We nevertheless had the same fine traits, the same height and oval faces. There was something boyish about her that I envied.

– Why do you keep repeating that as if it were a compliment? she had asked shortly after we met.

The explanation was simple, I guess.

My mother had made me feel, in a diffuse way, that she would have preferred having a son. I was an only child raised by nannies, both my parents travelling a great deal – for different purposes. While my father earned money, my mother spent it.

Adamant that I should not become unduly attached to anyone else, she submitted nannies to annual turnovers. No sooner had I become used to one than she was gone. Hugo once said that the protectiveness I inspire was due to my 'abandonic personality'. I did not like hearing this. It opened drawers I preferred to remain locked, convinced that selective repression is a survival strategy.

When I was a child, my mother would exhibit me like a doll in a puppet show after playing bridge or before a party.

– Look at her! Angel hair, turquoise eyes, a natural grace! Aleana, show us that ballet step! Turn! Bend! Smile!

It was awful. Secretly, at least at school, I tried to behave like a boy. But I was a quiet and eager learner, as girls are, even though my results were for several years hampered by dyslexia. That disorder was gone as suddenly as it had appeared.

My father and his twin sister, whom I worshipped, made me feel loved without any need for disguise or performance.

Well, that roughly sketched the family background – but not the ending up in hospital with a slashed wrist and a smitten heart. It was vital to understand why. All I know is that, by accident or aggression, this was the conclusion to one year of uncontrolled, downhill skidding.

*   *   *

A towering, wrinkled face leant over me. It took me a moment to realize where I was. The face belonged to an elderly man dressed in white.

– My name is Dr Klauser. I operated on you last night.

– Mine is Aleana.

– I know.

– How? Who brought me here?

– An ambulance called by your hotel. It seems that letting the bathtub overflow saved your life.

Tears cascaded down my cheeks. My feeling of shame became unbearable. Had I not been in this hospital, I'd be dead. That would have killed my father.

– Guilt is no remedy, said the doctor without compassion.

– Who knows about this? I mean . . .

– I'm no private detective, merely a surgeon. It took three hours repairing the harm you inflicted on yourself, consciously or not. It was touch and go, may I add.

– But why? Why?

– Precisely. A person who can help you answer that will call later.

– Who?

– Someone you can talk with freely.

– A goddamn shrink? I winced.

Dr Klauser looked irritated.

– Therapists are the cleansers of chaos and confusion. Not an easy job. Trust the one I send you. She's special and went through something tough too. All right?

– Yes, I whispered.

He examined my wrist, changed the bandage, and walked away loftily, humming 'Summertime'. Peculiar character, that doctor. The setting sun was projecting trembling shades on to the white wall. The bed next to mine was empty. No one in his right mind would have done what I seemingly had. Or else they would have succeeded, as decency requires.

Again, I tried to reassemble the puzzle of events.

The bathroom.

Get out of here! Leave me alone!

Victoria's cynical remarks.

Her leaving.

Finally, the phone ringing.

*   *   *

When I stepped out of the shower in Baden-Baden, Victoria was still leaning against the wall, facing the mirror. Was she absorbed in thought or merely smashed? The bottle of vodka was half empty.

– Look at you, she giggled, all ready for a moonlight serenade.

– I haven't seen Hugo for a whole year!

– He might be late because he swapped his car for a white horse.

– Very funny, Vic. Play fair.

– Be a good loser is what I'd recommend, she snapped.

– We've gone through that. Let's have dinner, okay?

– Dinner! As if I could swallow anything.

– Vodka seems to go down all right.

There were two armchairs in the vast bathroom, flanked by loudspeakers.

Victoria had chosen mellow jazz. Slightly ill at ease, I endeavoured to put on body-cream. Sitting down at last, she watched my every move. I went to the mini-bar and opened some champagne, determined to lift my spirits.

– You know, Vic, I think Hugo has sorted everything out.

– Really? His walk-in dressing room, or his walk-out bullshit?

– Stop it. He sounded, I don't know . . . relieved.

– I wonder why.

Victoria had been witnessing months of conversations over the phone and my corresponding mood-swings. At times, I felt confident and happy. At others, despondent. She considered Hugo an Italian playboy full of operetta sentimentalism. Never did she understand that it was only when Hugo came along that I rediscovered the unconditional love my father and aunt had offered me. In the meantime, I had looked for brothers in my relationships with men. Regarding sex as an accessory or a game, I had hurt feelings the sincerity of which I doubted. Victoria encouraged that scepticism, hers being even more cynical.

Still. I had agreed she accompany me to this ominous rendez-vous in Baden-Baden. In short, I was afraid.

– I'm glad you're here, Vic. Don't spoil it!

– Only one person can and will.

I gazed out of the window. The park was coloured in the shades of a splendid Indian summer. Dusk was descending on the picturesque town. People walked without haste, some pushing prams, others with satchels under one arm, many heading for the music kiosk. I noticed one old couple. She was stout but limping. He was small and wiry. The woman stumbled. The man tried to help her recover her balance. She pushed him away with a kick. It was an insult and a confession. It betrayed pain at getting to be invalid, a refusal of dependency, and the impulse to sweep aside, with one assassin's gesture, the companion of a lifetime.

– You'll be glad to find me here tomorrow, snickered Victoria.

– Why do you say that? Why be so negative all the time?

– Oh, no jealousy. Being twice removed, if you see what I mean, I'm a bit of a prophet, she added with sardonic modesty.

– Leave me in peace!

– Peace? she exclaimed. You don't even know what peace is!

– Precisely. I hunger for it.

She helped herself to another drink. I had one too. Somehow I could not get my make-up right. I sank into the other armchair thinking, time for that later.

The scene with the old couple had filled me with malaise. Victoria was following her own train of thoughts:

– The only protection against pain is to love two persons at the same time.

– Can you do that?

– You bet. Parallel lines meet at infinity.

– By then we're dead.

– So what? Things aren't as complicated or romantic as you think. We are taught to love a brother and a sister with different but similar feelings. Same with parents. Why should we change emotional attitudes outside the family?

– Vic . . .

– . . . what's wrong with bigamy – or bisexuality, for that matter? You tell me!

– Vic, must you be so belligerent?

– Yes! she cried, knocking over her armchair and pacing about the room. I can't just sit there and let that jerk blind you out of your wits! You're a gullible dreamer. Jolt out of your daft reveries!

Hugo crooned that you fit his ideal. But deep down he's a realist, and one who won't give up a comfortable nest to whisk you off on his wings.

– How can you say that? It's *too* cruel!

– Better be sad than sorry, darling.

Victoria's words hit me right where it hurt. Why on earth did I like her?

As we walked through deserted streets after the party at which we met, about a year earlier, she had asked:

– Where do you live?

– Round the corner.

– May I come in for the infamous 'one for the road'?

– Sure.

Perhaps she didn't notice the absence of walls or doors, the empty frames and blurred mirrors. Perhaps she didn't mind the symmetry of my disorder. Be that as it may, the conversation was easy. I told her about Hugo. No comments then either.

Next she asked me if she could have a bath. It was late and I suggested she stay overnight. The sheets of the guest room were in the laundry. My bed being huge, she could sleep at the other end. I am a deep sleeper.

Towards dawn, I felt her skin close to mine. It was soft and warm. Her hands reached out. Mine responded.

We saw each other sporadically during the next few months. I worked as a freelance journalist, Victoria as a dilettante model. But *our* night had generated complicity. We moved in the same circles and we reminded people of the 'Absolutely Fabulous' protagonists, with an ambiguous extra slant.

One day she phoned.

– Could I stay with you for a month? I'd be glad to share expenses.

– Okay, I said, but no longer than that.

I needed cash, and probably a friend. Besides, she was blatantly selfish, and I find selfish people restful.

Her haranguing about Hugo started soon thereafter. I sometimes wondered whether my interest in her was not a twisted desire to seduce someone both intimate and hostile as my mother had been.

All of this now seemed remote, also irrelevant. We were in Baden-Baden; Victoria was inebriated; my make-up was flawless, the telephone silent.

– Don't you understand that Hugo represents an antidote to your fear of failure?

– Past mistakes are no curse.

– You were always attracted to weak men in complicated situations. They make you feel good. When that doesn't work, they make you feel guilty. Hugo managed both. What about waking up, Aleana?

Like all drunks, she was getting repetitive, and on my nerves. She was also dead wrong

– He makes me feel normal, I sighed. Above all, wanted. Besides, he's the only man who gave me what others never did. I'm not used to being taken care of . . .

– Cared for, is what you mean. Why were you miserable for a whole year then?

– Because we couldn't be together, as you well know.

– Really? Don't other men manage to find time for their mistresses?

– He's not like other men and I'm not a mistress.

– That was many moons ago, she drawled. Hugo's cold and smooth like marble. Be prepared for the big chill.

– Leave me alone!

She walked towards the door, her gait dizzy.

– Alone? You'll never be alone.

Little do you know, I thought, as she slammed the door.

*   *   *

I have always lost my direction along paved ways. Some children need to brush or grope reality in a tentative manner before finding their place in it. Later they learn how to steer their lives, just as they learnt to walk. Soft obstacles and smooth impacts allow them to ascertain parameters. The predictable alternation of privation and rewards moulds their consciousness. I, on the other hand, always needed a shock or a crash. It was quicker but harsh and lonely.

Sports commentators sometimes mention 'the Indian syndrome', referring to a signal that establishes, at the very beginning of the confrontation between athletes and forever after, a secret hierarchy, a fascination for the inevitable loss, a surrender of the spirit. Why fight? The dice are tossed. That's how it is and this is how it will always be.

All of a sudden I missed my father, wanted to call him, but discarded the desire. Wasn't I grown up at thirty-three?

I remembered his waiting for me at Vienna's airport some weeks earlier. In the midst of a coarse, fat-bellied crowd, he looked frail, like a distracted gentleman wandered into the wrong century. He wore a tie I had given him for his birthday. I wore a shawl he gave me for mine. Both our faces lit up on seeing each other. No kissing or hugging: my father is not that kind of person. But his eyes did both.

I wish he had been there right then in the bathroom, reading in the armchair Vic had leapt out of in front of an already pitch-dark scenery. Then the telephone rang as shrill as a siren.

– *Amore?* It's me.

  – Hugo! At last! Where are you?

  – There was an accident on the road. Must be back in Strasburg first thing in the morning. It's so late I'm not sure I shouldn't turn round.

  – Do what?

He sounded embarrassed.

  – Aleana, what I have to say can perhaps be said over the phone.

  – Oh no! I've waited for so long! Please tell me later! I must see and hug and feel you again, my love!

Silence. Was I wrong, or was there a shadow of impatience in the silence?

– Listen. Things are not as easy as you think. Actually they are terribly difficult.

– But Hugo! You promised . . . I mean . . . last time we spoke you said . . .

– I know. But something unforeseen happened.

– Didn't you get your embassy in Madrid?

– That's not it.

– What is it then? I implored, knowing full well the requirement for breezy casualness.

Hugo hesitated. Whatever he had to say he was finding it hard.

– Family matters.

– Your stepfather and his emotional blackmail?

– No . . .

– So what's going on?

– My wife is pregnant.

– Your wife . . . is what . . . ?

I felt like an alpinist whose hearing becomes impaired by distance and fog. I also felt blind. A child was destined to come to life and required the burial of our future. My anguish collided with anger.

At the other end, Hugo's voice seemed worlds removed, unreal and muddled. Something about the passing of time, the toll taken by responsibilities, the beauty of our memories and so on and so forth. He kept asking if I was still there. What could I *not* answer? That I was, always would be? Unable to breathe, I could not speak. Last thing I remember, as in a sleepwalking haze, was his saying:

– Don't move. I'll be there as fast as I can.

This is where it all gets blurred. *Et pour cause*, I fear.

Instead of hanging up, I stumbled to the bathroom door. It was locked on the outside. I panicked.

As a child I had been locked in my room as a punishment. When I lost my parents in an airport, the police locked me in what seemed a cell. Once I had been stuck in a lift for a whole night. The lesson I derived from such situations was that captivity is weakness and the turned key means being a hostage. I never believed that doors or partitions, walls or bars were synonymous with safety. Behind them, solitude is rape and silence surrender. Be it in a bathroom, a prison or a role.

Why was that door locked? Why was Hugo not next to me, as he had said he would be, over and over, forever and more?

Then:

I reached for whatever bottle was at hand, not so much to drink as to keep my mouth shut. I felt like screaming, sobbing, swearing. I felt a numb but open wound. What else?

The ceiling spun as I opened my eyes again. Hugo had said all he could say. It was over. I was alone, and for good. See him? What for? To suffer more? Impossible. This was rock bottom. Reality down here felt like quicksand, problem being that the sinking is slow. Then . . . Then I searched Vic's beauty-case and found what I needed. Tranquillizers – or so I assumed. I knocked several down with whatever it was. Opened the tap. I needed a bath. I always need water when in distress. I need to float. If only it were more often on the surface than not. I tried to remove my make-up but thought of the movie stars who wake up after a night of tears or passion looking impeccable, so why bother? In any case, my hands no longer responded to my control. The phone ringing again shook me out of my torpor. Instead of reaching for it, I ambled towards the door. It was locked. I had forgotten that. Panic set my heart running amok. Why should Vic have taken the key, introduced it on the other side, and turned it? From the drawing room came frantic and weird music. She must have been a goner by then.

I was locked out because I was locked in. The laminating pain felt like a razor and a blade. What would help? Another pill? Another sip of vodka? Beyond that, a blank.

*   *   *

Then, without transition, the walls of a hospital room.

– My name is Iris.

What was this – a cocktail party or a convention? Whoever appeared at my bedside introduced themselves in an almost comical way considering the surroundings.

– How do you do? I answered in a manner equally civil.

– Dr Klauser told you I'd come to pay a visit, I think.

– Are you the shri . . . the therapist?

– I am.

Well into her fifties, one could see how beautiful she must have been. Her charm had survived, perhaps even been enhanced by, the passing of time. In any case, she hardly corresponded to my stereotyped picture of the gaunt, stern, highbrowed psycho-whatever.

Why wasn't Victoria there? Where was Hugo?

– Has nobody come to see me since last night? I asked in what I realized was a pleading voice.

– I don't know. But they would not have been allowed in. You need to recover

– Do my parents know . . . about . . . well . . . ?

– Not unless you want us to inform them. You are an adult.

I felt a dwarf and a failure. If that was being grown up, thanks. Iris watched and waited. I had always associated shrinks with teeth pullers who would inflict acute pain on the grounds it was the price to pay for relief. Iris just sat there and would not have surprised me if she had started knitting.

– Who is Hugo? she casually asked.

– How do you know about him?

– I sat next to you in the post-operatory room. You kept calling him.

– Oh.

Much to my dismay, I could not repress tears as they shot out again.

– He's the first man I really loved.

– Lucky you, she said softly.

– What?

– Many people never love, not even once.

– What about you? I asked, mainly to delay talking about myself.

– I loved only once. He died in a plane crash . . .

I remembered Dr Klauser hinting that the therapist he would send had 'been there' too.

– And then?

She gazed out of the window.

– Aren't I the one who asks questions?

The truth is that I felt as near as I could to being relaxed.

– Tell me about Hugo.

– Is that necessary?

– Would I ask if it weren't?

Where and how to begin? Hugo's personality didn't help.

– I met Hugo in Rome, almost exactly a year ago. It was a banal encounter. We had dinner in one of those pretentious restaurants where even chicken are cross-legged. Hugo was one of a group of mutual friends. We sat together at one end of the table and might as well have been alone. It was . . . lovely. At some point I emptied my handbag looking for my lip-gloss. Among the bits and pieces I extracted there was a telephone bill. Hugo took it.

– I shouldn't think his intention was to pay it . . .

– Who knows? I smiled back, cheered by her off-handed humour.

– He called you?

– The next day. We hardly parted for the following three months, except at night . . .

– Married?

– Yes. You might think that fuelled our passion. Obstacles and secrecy often do. But to me it doesn't account for the sense of, well, *belonging* that we both felt. We were on the same wavelength. As with many clichés, it was absolutely true. We liked the same authors, the same composers, the same paintings. He could read my thoughts as I anticipated his. Everything seemed easy and natural. The fact that his family had left to spend the summer on

Capri helped, of course. He'd join them at weekends, but those breaks allowed us to recover from the intensity of our feelings. You cannot imagine how happy I was, Iris!

She gazed at the trees. Their branches hissing in the wind filled the silence with silky whispers. Was I unwittingly scratching wounds?

– Go on, she said after a while.

– What can I say that you haven't already imagined? At times the joy of reciprocated love transfused us so that we were oblivious of time and space. At others, our awareness of outside factors was so acute we held on to the moment as if to a buoy. Bliss was always tinged with fear, but a delicious fear.

– Adultery always has a component of forbidden games, of returning to some paradise lost. The agony of separations followed by fusion's incandescence, she mused, as if speaking to herself. Innocent love in adult situations is pyromaniac.

I laughed a bittersweet laugh. Not even shrinks were immune from melodramatic kitsch.

– And then?

– The summer ended. His family came back. Indiscretion had caused his stepfather to get wind of the affair. First he dismissed it as a typical adventure like the sort many Italian men have during holidays, which ends thereafter. But it had turned into a passion. Hugo was prepared to give up career, family and all. I dissuaded him. Not out of saintly altruism, but because I feared he might regret decisions taken on impulse. I was wrong, and regret it now more bitterly than I can say.

– Why?

– Because I was wrong, I repeated emphatically. A woman in love mustn't ever leave the side of the man she loves.

– Why not?

– Because she'll lose him, I sniffed.

*   *   *

Iris was gone. Night had fallen. Only twenty-four hours had

elapsed since my checking into the hotel with Victoria, less since his phone calls and my . . . madness.

A patchwork of Hugo's letters formed in my memory. Thinking of Iris, and desperate for some occupation, I wrote it all down in the haphazard way it came back into my mind.

Nothing will prevent me from loving you. Nothing will prevent us from being together again and forever. But my love, I am unable to change things as fast as the dream that inhabits us requires. You are right: for your sake, for mine and for the future, I wouldn't want to 'patch' things up at the price of a minefield or, more pathetically, of scandal. You have no idea of the changes that occurred in these three months of togetherness . . . Since I have fallen into the void of your absence, I feel amputated. Our rapture was no factor of stolen moments and clandestine ardour; it was as it was because it had to be . . . Once overwhelmed, we had to surrender, and now we belong to each other, come what may . . . Be strong, be patient, be yourself. Never change, for I love you just as you, and as we are . . . When we met, I had abdicated what is essential to me. You restored my ideals. Until we met my life had become a cortège of compromises, denials and disguises. I lived in tepid waters. I can now face ice and fire. I can move again *all at once* . . . You are not used to the harassment of society that I, being an accomplice to partial manipulation, know only too well . . . I have exposed you to pain and solitude, but darling, it won't be long before I can make up for it . . .

A disturbing thought made my handwriting shaky. It made me shiver just as the sight of the old couple by the lake had the day before.

Those lyrical letters were written in the months following our parting in October, after all hell broke loose. Hugo had sent me a mobile phone for Christmas, with a note saying he couldn't stand not reaching me day or night. Sadly, this present none the less stopped all correspondence on his part. Should I have listened to Vic, who as usual had not minced her words?

– Honey, the guy's withdrawing. Prudent or scared, what's the difference? Sure he loved you, sure he'll cherish the memory as long as he lives and all that jazz. But sooner or later he'll call less often, just as he's stopped writing. He'll find excuses. Life, etc., the burden his guilt would inflict upon your frail shoulders and some such crap. Wait and see.

Had she been right? Had she foreseen that eternal love would be eroded by daily priorities and convenience? That our summer of passion would be reduced to a burden, the memory of it to nothing but an impressionist painting destined to fade? Victoria had also predicted that Hugo's feelings wouldn't prevent him making love to his wife.

I had swept aside these images, simply too bleak to endure.

The Baden-Baden episode must have opened my eyes with such a blinding flash that I had felt unable to face it, and so I cut myself off from reality by cutting my wrist.

Barren thoughts among white walls that suddenly felt like black curtains. Iris. What would she make of all this? I looked forward to talking to her. I needed her. I need others too often and too much.

*   *   *

She came early next morning. I showed her what I had written. She asked whether I would agree to a graphology analysis. I did. What could I risk that I hadn't lost already? She called the nurse and gave instructions.

– It will take a couple of hours.

I sighed. It isn't pleasant to know one's soul is being submitted to a subjective X-ray. On the other hand, I was curious to know what would come out of it. In a peculiar way I was beginning to feel like the reader of a story eager to discover the outcome of a plot that concerns and eludes mainly himself. Once I had answered various questions about my background, where I lived and what I did, she proceeded in her usual casual way (as if anything was anodyne or casual any more):

– Tell me about your family.

– Oh well . . . My father is a father, and also my best friend. His support has always been indiscriminate. Excessive? Perhaps. In any case, it compensates for my mother's rejection. She condemns my disregard for conventions and envies my apparent lightness of being.

– I would have thought natural gravity pulls you down . . .

– In other circumstances, I can be vivacious and frivolous, though you may find it hard to believe! Thing is, I'm a bit of a cocktail . . . insecure but trusting, solitary and sociable in equal measures . . . truth being I don't know who I am really. A kind of double-faced Janus, turning her back on herself, perhaps . . .

That made Iris gasp. After a thoughtful pause, she said:

– You'll recover, Aleana, not least for being so articulate.

– If you're right, isn't that the saddest thing of all about it?

Iris took a pad and a pencil, put on horn-rimmed glasses and looked her part. Friendly banter was over.

– Correct me if I'm wrong. My impression is as follows: your definition of yourself is always two negatives that cancel one another out. You emphasize being bilingual and multicultural. You are as emotional as you are cerebral. You seduce women but can love only one man. You write but demean your talent. Etcetera. You keep opposing the South and the North but will not place yourself at some psychological equator. Many choices, many facets, but ultimately, despondency and disorientation. Why not describe yourself as a sum total rather than a subtraction of your halves?

– Could you translate for the simple-minded – sorry, the 'mentally challenged' as I think one says nowadays?

– See? she teased. What I mean is that you locked yourself up in a suffocating binary system. That without your ambiguous and damaging relationship with your mother or Victoria, the relationship with Hugo might not have found fertile ground. I also mean we must all come to terms with contradictory and sometimes conflicting aspects of our personalities. Can't you, or won't you?

– I don't know.

The truth is I didn't.

– Right. Tell me more about Hugo.

– It's difficult to verbalize someone you know too well.

– Do make an effort, Aleana.

– Well . . . At first, he reminded me of a snail without a shell – nothing to do with a slow pace, but a lot with seeming to move unprotected, you know . . . I felt he needed a shelter around him, and probably longed to provide some such thing to him. He never talked about his past, except in a fragmented way. Discretion and decency forbade him to blame anyone or anything for the feeling of inadequacy he seemed to suffer from.

– Inadequacy?

– Yes. Hugo felt the casting was wrong. He had to suppress his true inclinations, which were artistic, in order to assume the role imparted to him. Hugo was an actor who neither fitted the costume nor believed in the props. His sense of urgency, his idealism, his craving for authenticity made him despise the disguise tailoring his behaviour. Having embodied a mirror, I might have been a threat. Does that sound very muddled?

– No. But I must ask you something that might hurt. Could it be that you represented an obligation to commitment, requiring a choice, both of which he felt disinclined to do, lest it might destroy the frail foundations of pretence he had been forced to consolidate?

– Who knows? I never understood what he really feared. Without being an egocentric, he admired little about others– except those extremely close to him – and less about himself.

– '*Il se méprisait à grands cris joyeux*'?

– That's it, I murmured.

Iris seemed not only to share my leaning towards Baudelaire but also put her mind's finger on a quintessential facet of Hugo's personality. It led to a flashback. I shivered again.

– What is it you remember? Iris asked with an intent glance.

– Something that always puzzled me, but . . . I don't want to talk about it.

– Please, Aleana, try. It's important. For both of you.

Did she mean both of my halves, or Hugo and me? I hesitated. When truth isn't a fence, it's a one-way street. I also had the feeling that evoking these images would be like raping his intimacy.

– Whenever he was angry or frustrated, he would tear things like newspapers or cigarettes apart, in a strangely mechanical, almost hypnotic way. Or else he would go to the kitchen and cut an apple or a bread loaf into small pieces. At first I thought it was a relief for overstrained nerves held constantly in check by breeding or necessity. Yet it kind of scared me

– Did he ever get violent with you?

– With me? I exclaimed with indignation. You must be joking! He never – ever! – was violent with anyone, not even verbally. Which is why I thought he needed weird outlets to a depressive rage I could understand, but unfortunately couldn't soothe.

Hugo's arms around me, his loving eyes, his swapping a sports car for an automatic one only to be able to touch my hand while driving, flooded me with infinite nostalgia. I had felt helpless before, but here, in this clinic, with no one but a professional listener to talk to, I felt more impotent than ever.

– Please change the subject, Iris.

– Would you like to rest?

– How could I?

– Then let's start at the beginning. You are an only child. Your mother loves but does not accept you. Your father loves you but doesn't express it. You turn to your aunt for maternal love, and to lovers for brotherly feelings. In women you taunt the mother you miss, in men you seek the father you can't replace.

– Wait a minute!

– Let me continue. Then we'll talk. All right?

– All right.

– Since you cannot reconcile, you multiply. Victoria, for instance, is a masculine woman. Hugo is a feminine man. One devours but resents you; the other loves and abandons you. Both are predictable experiences, since we unwillingly reproduce the same pain, mainly because it is familiar.

– In other words, it is patterns I duplicate rather than pairs I collect?

Iris laughed. It almost felt like having an ally, certainly not like being exposed to judgement or censure.

– You're a fast learner.

– Too late.

– It never is.

That's what people say, I thought bitterly.

People! Where were they? Both Hugo and Vic must have known where I was and why. Alone.

Before Iris walked out, I asked her whether visits where now permitted.

– Of course, she said, then hesitated, having read thoughts she was unable to sweep aside.

I closed my eyes. Next thing I knew, the sun was rising.

*　　*　　*

After an insipid breakfast, I picked up the phone and, indeed, got a line. I dialled the number of the Principe Hotel. Needless to say I simply asked for Room 308.

– The ladies left, I was succinctly told.

– Even Ms Victoria Bellon?

– Just a second . . . yes, she left a while ago with her husband. Can I help you?

– No thank you.

A strange thing happened that often happens to me after having a nightmare: I was shaken by merriment. Not a bitter or hysterical laugh; a hearty laughter. The concept of Hugo and Vic leaving together, possibly in a car trailing empty cans, or rather empty vodka bottles, filled me with mirth. Still . . . the back of my mind was petrified. Vic was capable of seducing anyone to win a bet, be it against me. She knew no scruples. Her idea of 'getting away with murder' – an expression of her predilection – was a perfect crime with no corpse. Consequences were something she had neither the habit nor the nerve to face.

Hugo might have arrived after I'd done . . . what I did. Vic might have invented some plausible story about my storming off, or else she might have said I'd tried to kill myself and, a scandal being unthinkable in his position, she'd help him out, even provide a false alibi should there be an investigation.

In either scenario she could have succeeded in manipulating him: perhaps out of spite, because our erotic games had meant more than *coquetterie* to her, as I had come to realize; or simply out of control-freakness. Talk about love turning to hatred! Never did my gut feelings switch from doubt into disgust as rapidly as in that hospital bed.

Vic's actual name, as she conveniently pointed out when trying to impress certain gentlemen, was Marie-Victoire. She had dropped the Marie, quite rightly so – it suited her as a boxing glove would suit a nun – and changed Victoire to Victoria. Her idol was Victoria Lake.

I recalled her obsession with her hands, which she kept putting into cream-filled gloves. They truly were beautiful.

She once said hands see faster than eyes.

– Is that why you tend to watch women with yours? I had joked.

– Possibly, she replied. I often wonder what is more telling about us, our hands or what they behold, our manicured fingers or their capacity to strangle . . .

She was dead serious, and her husky voice sent a shiver down my spine. Plotting and scheming were a poker game for her, and as with any game, it was one she would rather cheat at than lose. All things considered, she wasn't just a witty, brainy, spoilt brat; she was a shit. Endlessly talking, greedily taking, always on the lookout for a new toy, preferably human, so she could pull its strings.

Was I being unfair? Mad? Were my thoughts too flippant not to be true? I certainly wasn't laughing any more.

I switched on the television, but could not concentrate. Instead, kaleidoscopic visions of another nature scrambled in my eyes:

Vic and Hugo stop to have a drink, exchange confidences, getting warmer, closer and confused. Their knees touch, their hands meet. Vic's voluminous and teasing breasts shine in the dim light; she has exaggerated that sparking body gel again. Hugo tells her about his guilt and our summer passion. She confesses the ambiguity of her friendship with me. It sounds enticing, like a secret. Her smile is both perverse and innocent. She is her beguiling self to the point of kitsch. Hugo feels the trap, but willingly dances around it, with calculated silences rather than words.

Suddenly it all becomes delirious. They are alone in that bar which looks like a Visconti set: crimson velvets, baroque angels in Bacchus attitudes, erotic variations on classical music. Their shadows spin in a vertiginous embrace. There is something not only decadent but sadomasochistic in the air. They look like two addicts spiralling in a feverish pace from withdrawal to overdose. Gradually at first, then violently, both abandon themselves to desire, its cruelty and its imperatives. He unzips her dress.

She lets his fingers wander. They feel their heartbeats accelerate by touching their wrists. Their blood streams towards that knot in the plexus where all differences between men and women implode. She licks his neck, he bites her lips. They no longer see each other, transfixed in some shrine where sex and mind turn into black magic.

Are they going to make love? No. What has love got to do with it? These two are breathlessly pursuing pleasure, but each on their own, in their own obsessive way. In their panting race towards extremes, they compete instead of meeting. Their impatience isn't generous, their skins aren't attuned.

Like a jinn, I leap from out of nowhere, facing them.

– There are people who say that suffering ennobles. This is not true, I scream.

I am dressed to kill. To destroy the spell. To annihilate.

– Ah, snaps Victoria, I should have expected you intruding!

– Darling, I reply cattishly, there is no *sortilège* without sacrilege, didn't you teach me that?

Hugo looks flabbergasted. What do I care? Since it has come this far, I want to be a part of it. Be it only as a *voyeuse*. Staring at Hugo, I languidly undress Victoria. A striptease by proxy, if you will. With a vengeance.

Still staring at Hugo, I whisper:

– More women? More victims? More casualties? Fine.

Whereupon I take Vic by the hand, hesitating whether to be gentle or throw her on to the floor. I become prey to a thrilling dizziness. I sense Hugo's morbid fascination in my veins.

– I'll offer you Vic like a sacrificed idol forced to worship a malefic god. Watch!

Half pimp and half accomplice, I display the lethal combination of feminine delicacy with masculine violence. In other words, I do what men do, the way women dream of. Quite a spectacle, if I may immodestly say so.

I was prey and hunter, whore and nurse. Amid the whisper of skins, the rustle of satins, the murmur of sensitivities, my angry heart sleepwalked on a rope too tight not to snap. Why does nobody say 'crash in love'?

Which is when I fell apart, in torrential tears.

*   *   *

It took me a while to calm down. Those goddamn white walls reassured me this once. I felt feverish and confused. Heaven or hell knows why, I started humming the song, 'Last night I had a dream', addressed to a figure more scary even than the vampire and ghost the dream also contained.

– You like Randy Newman's songs too?

Iris stood next to my bed. She sat down with a suspiciously smooth manner.

– What is it that really scares you the most?

– What a question coming from a shrink! Myself. What else?

– The shrink, as you call me, doesn't wholly believe that.

– Oh?

– Don't be sarcastic. Don't pretend to feel guilty, for you shouldn't. What you do suffer from most of all is disillusion. As to guilt and remorse, they are two feelings you must learn to disentangle.

– You mean fantasies as opposed to facts?

– More or less.

I felt irascible. This lady never took the risk of confrontation.

– As far as I am concerned, Iris, behaviour moulds itself on experience and its interpretation, whereas character is destiny.

– Can you explain what you mean?

– It's crystal clear, for Christ's sake! Why don't *you* explain? To begin with, could you really tell me what happened in that bathroom?

A sudden fierce exasperation had thrust itself upon me. She took my hand. An infallible way to calm me down normally, but nothing was normal at that point . . .

– Because helping you entails stepping back. If you close up, we will both have failed. But I will tell you this: you swallowed a high dosage of Flunitrazepam, marketed as Rohypnol. It's a *killer* – and not as a figure of speech. It accounts for about ninety per cent of suicides implicating sleeping-pills over the last two decades.

It was my turn to gasp – with horror.

– In three quarters of accidental cases, death is due to drowning, typically in a bath-tub.

– Jesus!

– It's God you must thank, Aleana, because, combined with alcohol, it can cause respiratory coma, muscle paralysis or cardiac arrest. Same as any overdose.

– How do you know that's what I took? I winced, in a last, feeble and desperate attempt to deny the gravity of my action.

– Simple. It being the strongest hypnotic anxiolytic around, a single dose of it can be detected up to five days after administration, and you provided more than enough blood to take samples from.

Could it get worse? It could.

– Finally – and I only deliver this speech to make quite sure you'll never, ever take chemicals light-heartedly – even without alcohol, Rohypnol induces anterograde amnesia almost immediately, which is why it is also known as the 'rape drug'.

She sighed, visibly affected.

– Rohypnol is currently being rescheduled to Schedule I from Schedule III on the FDA's scale of psychotropic substances and no longer available in doses superior to one milligram. I wish it were taken off the market altogether. The stuff's dynamite. You were lucky.

Tears rolled down my cheeks again.

– I'll leave you to rest for a while, but not for long. I don't think you should be alone right now. Okay?

Without expecting a sign of life, she slipped away.

Poor Iris. I was no easy patient, and she obviously was still in mourning over her own 'only love'. I had given her a hard time. The thought made me feel even more shitty.

My recent life seemed to have followed a motion similar to a revolving door – or rather, to spirals, cycles, cyclones . . . rejection followed by the feeling of rejection. What had alarmed me before now paled into insignificance compared to recent folly.

Moments later, the moon-faced nurse gave me a sedative. She also changed my bandage, said: 'Excellent!' and removed the drip in my arm. I then ran to the bathroom, anxious to see if I'd recognize myself. Not only did I look the same, but rested. Even that was painful: I felt I didn't deserve to look so well.

When Iris walked back in, I tried to act as composedly as a shattered person can.

– Are you all right?

– Yes, Iris. Forgive me for my impatience, and thanks for your honesty. It's . . . a shock, but I have always needed detonators to snap out of . . . whatever it is that messes me up. But deep down, I do believe that the platform where true progress begins is accessible. I am not the disenchanted wreck my situation suggests, please believe me. You're doing your best and it's certainly an improvement on anything I can do. Yet . . .

– The best is never good enough, is it?

We looked at each other and laughed the way one cries without warning.

– So what do you intend do about it?

– About what? Love? Hugo? Victoria? Life, to put it in a nutshell? No idea.

– Life can't be reduced to love, Aleana.

– I heard the rumour.

– More difficult than learning to give is learning to receive. There is more to life than seeking recognition or displaying tolerance, not least towards oneself. There are important things that . . .

Providentially, some moustached personage interrupted this somewhat awkward dialogue. Iris scrutinized the papers he handed to her. She then looked me straight in the eye, all trace of feigned aloofness gone. Although appearing uneasy, in a strange way she also looked jubilant.

– What's the matter now? I inquired almost querulously.

She stared at me, with startling intensity.

– Were you ever aware of being left-handed as a child? she asked.

– Very much so. My first nannies used to put my left hand in a skiing glove, the type without fingers, you know, in order to prevent me using it. My right hand was the 'right' one to use, according to the educational imperative.

– Were you allowed to use it at all? inquired Iris, now in her professional mode, taking notes, spectacles and all.

– What kills us is not the disease. What kills us, dear doctor, are the remedies, I smiled mischievously.

– Aleana, answer my question!

Her tone was authoritative. I like to bend to authority and postponed flippancy to a more appropriate moment.

– I did indeed hold my tennis racket or toothbrush with

the hand that felt most comfortable. These things didn't seem important. Important were things like writing, using forks and knives, all the social stuff I was trained to care about. Why?

– The graphologist's analysis is categorical. You may find its conclusion uncomfortable.

– I am in no comfortable position anyway, Iris.

– Since you are no fool, I will spare you a long lecture about the consequences of being an impeded left-handler, one of which is dyslexia. The point is that, under considerable strain or stress, in nearly unconscious states, left-handers, however conditioned they may be to use their right hand to do the so-called 'right' things, instinctively revert to the use of their left hand.

– Meaning?

– Meaning that if you had, on impulse or instinct, wanted to slash your wrist, you would have damaged the right wrist using your left hand. Get it?

I did. The impact left me numb.

If I hadn't cut my veins, who had, and why? I needed silence. I needed to be alone. This was too much for a single day – the third in this hospital? I had lost track..

– Don't worry, Aleana. All will be well, she whispered before tiptoeing out of the room.

You must be kidding, I thought, my emergency antennae on red alert.

* * *

The awareness of being a specialist in beginnings leading nowhere has tormented me for years. Now, instead of drifting, floating or hanging, I stood at a crossroads that seemed a tunnel. This was no place to wait and say, I'll deal with it later. I had to understand right here and now how I'd ended in so demented a situation. I repressed another nervous laugh as I determined to proceed by elimination to solve my 'suicidal homicide', a new concept in crime. 'Who dunnit, if not me?'

The old bitch whose assassin gesture towards her lifelong companion so dismayed me, who had limped into the hotel to kill a woman younger that she'd ever be again? The elegant lady and the younger man in my delirious dream who, having failed to stab me, followed my tracks: quite a tricky manoeuvre for an absent mother and a fictitious brother. All of it nicely baroque, but preposterous.

Supposing the graphologist was right – and as I mentioned at the beginning, I did suffer from dyslexia for several years – then only two persons came into the equation. Both had the opportunity. Had I not discovered Hugo had come to Baden-Baden and left with Vic? Now: who had the motive?

Victoria?

It came back to me little by little, then in leaps and bounds. Plagued by my own sense of worthlessness, or low self-esteem, I had never fully realized she was jealous of me all along. First, she was obsessed with not being seductive to men, being rather masculine, not so much in looks as in demeanour. She envied my femininity, perhaps even my vulnerability, and probably my friendship with my father. Victoria's had rejected her for power. He disapproved of her explosive lust for power and had put her on a remote shelf, together with some quicksilver moonstones one admires but would rather not approach. In a neurotic moment, she had told me she would have preferred having a conflict-ridden relationship with a bitchy mother rather than a non-existent one with an alcoholic one too dazed to care.

Then came secondary causes like the fact of my having a worthwhile job whereas hers was nothing but a narcissistic pastime; or the fact I needed work to settle bills, which she didn't, even though I owned a home, while she didn't . . . things like that. Did 'having it all' without actually owning anything explain that compulsive obsession with her hands?

More important, more complex, was her animosity towards Hugo. I now wondered whether she had been jealous of that relationship too. Nothing else could explain such persistent denigration of someone unknown. Was her anger directed at me, for inspiring passion, or at him, for reciprocating it – so long as he did?

To cut a long story short, she could have slashed my wrist – obviously the wrong wrist – for all sorts of reasons, not least her being utterly drunk. Or – Christ! – she would have put the Rohypnol pills on the top of her beauty-case for me to find and take. This possibility was so plausible I needed to discard the thought, as if jumping off a roof to forestall vertigo spinning through my head.

Hugo?

Again I could not help but remember his fits of frustration when he used scissors or knives to shred trivial objects to pieces. Had I become a trivial, cumbersome object? One that stood in his way, burdened his conscience, smirched his guilty mind with promises un-held? Could he have fallen in some kind of mental crevasse, seeing me unconscious and bleeding, the image of misery and humiliation? Would he have freaked, taken a blade, and removed his guilt by transferring it? Not to kill me, of that I was more than convinced, but to remove the memory?

What if his wife had followed him and paid the butler to do it? Yes, not a good one, but I was drifting. All of this seemed too surrealistic. Yet . . . if anything is possible, none of it was plausible. Suddenly I remembered a strange dialogue, while leaning on the balustrade of his beautiful flat on Piazza Navona, deserted at dawn.

– One day, Hugo had said, we will have a house with a tropical garden.

– Near the sea? I had smiled.

– The sea is always close to happiness.

– If only this could come true!

– Dreams come true are treacherous blessings, my love. Just imagine, some years on, watching me from your window as I stroll towards the gate, as I would every morning, to collect the mail. You will know me by heart by then. However – during a split second, that man with whom you share night and day might seem a stranger. The very tranquillity of the sight will transform that second into the most devastating doubt.

– Why? Why should reality fall apart for no reason?

– Because you will realize I did remain a stranger. Love is no cure for ultimate solitude. Because a single, almost imperceptible pain restores all the distances we behold. Because knowing how fragile the boundaries are between the visible and the invisible, we cling to illusions, the sentinels of our hopes.

(Had this acid tale been a diplomatic warning?)

All of this was nauseating.

But then, after all, Iris wasn't infallible either. After so many years of using my right hand in most situations, I might very well have automatically used it in Baden-Baden too – or wouldn't I?

I remembered a *New Yorker* cartoon. It depicted a larva creeping out of the sea, then crawling, looking around, then adapting, becoming a man walking around with a suit and an attaché case. All of a sudden, he stops sharp. Realizing what he has become, he steps backwards, horror-struck, from one stage to the former, until returning to the sea in his initial larval state.

I got dressed, sneaked out of the hospital, and decided to forget in order to survive. And to laugh, as much as life would permit. I would never know the truth, the whole truth and nothing but the truth. Being so often two-faceted or double-edged, it is sometimes best ignored.

Charly's Château, January 2002

2

Quit
or The Man who Most Hurt my Pride

'His first rush of inarticulate resentment had been followed
by a steadiness and concentration of tone more disconcerting
to Lily than the excitement preceding it. For a moment her
presence of mind forsook her . . . To gain time she repeated:
"I don't understand what you want."

'Trenor had pushed a chair between herself and the door.
He threw himself in it and leaned back, looking up at her.
"I'll tell you what I want; I want to know just where you and I
stand. Hang it, the man who pays for the dinner is generally
allowed to have a seat at the table."'

– Edith Wharton, *The House of Mirth*

The wedding ceremony had been short, to the relief of most.
September in the South of France can still be very hot. In the
small church perched above the picturesque village of Mougins,
someone had read from Corinthians in a way that moved me . . .
not only the moving passage itself, but the voice.

Added to that was the emotion of recognizing many faces, and
noticing discreet tears in the bride's father's eyes. The elegance of
this exuberant crowd magazines call 'the beautiful people', who
on occasion rise to the cliché, was stunning. Actually, this was a
gathering of old friends, their wives, girlfriends and even some of
their children.

Some had travelled long distances. Others like Brian, the newly
wed, had crossed dire straights. Faced with the crash of Lloyds,
volatile markets or ruinous divorces, the British 'happy few' who
were twenty-something in the 'sixties had discovered with a bang
that education based on excellence in sports had its flaws.

Brian was a very special friend to me, not only because our friendship went back twenty tears, but because his debonair manner had remained unaltered, his sense of humour intact. He had lately fallen in love and was now married, possibilities hitherto dismissed with bemusement by his chums and former hangers-on. Everyone presented a boisterous gaiety. It all brought back happy memories of my student years in London.

There were three days of celebration ahead. I gazed at the sea beyond majestic pine trees, feeling thirsty. A bloody Mary, Brian's breakfast for as long he could remember, was what I was heading for when someone intentionally impeded my progress.

– I have been looking for you. Weren't you in church?

– Of course I was! I replied.

– I didn't see you.

– We arrived late.

The plural 'we' usually proved smart in cutting off masculine interest. But here evidently was one not to be deterred by trivialities.

– Too bad. I think I did quite a good reading.

With abundant greying hair, distinguished, neither tall nor short, neither thin nor fat, the overall impression Christopher conveyed was one of strength. He bore the kind of haughty confidence one would have called arrogant had it not been unaffected. His eyes were a pallid, frosty blue. He laughed without smiling.

A bit of caricature, I thought, noticing the signet ring and the monogrammed shirt with a crown. I glanced back at the various groups, wondering which to join before all made a leap to a table for lunch.

Christopher was now pointing at the programme of the ceremony.

– Never use that title. Rather embarrassing that Brian should have.

– Really? Then why mention it?

I spotted a good friend and steered in her direction, closely followed by my self-appointed escort. Everyone knew everyone, so after a long preamble of effusion we sat down. By now a little effort towards my unshakeable admirer was only polite. Question a man about himself if you want to engage in vivacious conversation.

– How have you been? I know we met before but don't quite . . .

– We met twenty years ago, my dear. Since then . . .

Twenty minutes later, I knew all about his two broken marriages, his professional ups and downs and now the loneliness at the top – 'you know what I mean'. I didn't. He had informed me about the clauses of his life insurance, about tax havens, about his skis needing mending, about his new car . . . Finally, having heard him repeat twice that he did not tolerate his name being abbreviated to Chris, I turned an icy shoulder.

Intense people are fascinating in certain situations, but this was not one of them. I had been looking forward to some good laughs and flippant conversations. The occasion, after all, was a reunion of old friends getting older but not much wiser, alcohol being a selective conservative. I enjoyed the copper sunshine and the mild September breeze.

No chance with Christopher. He was now detailing a résumé of his family's history, the chivalrous origins of which were fascinating, and entertaining too, for he spoke well and the wine helped.

– Do you like boats?

– I love boats.

– Splendid.

Why? I wondered without caring. It had been a long lunch. A late dinner stood ahead. By now everybody moved from one table to another; some danced, others ended up in the pool or on the nearby beach.

I sneaked away, back to one of the small hotels that had been booked for the event. Time for a siesta.

Hardly an hour later the phone rang.

– Hi there. Rested?

– Who's that?

– Christopher.

– Christopher who?

My sense of repartee, or mere politeness, is nil when I'm woken up indelicately.

– It's me, for heaven's sake. Dinner is at the harbour later on. I don't suppose you are organized, so I'll fetch you at nine.

– Oh?

What on earth gave him the impression I wouldn't have made a thousand plans? As a matter of fact, I hadn't, but what a cheeky thing to say to a girl like me!

– By the way, I also chartered a boat for tomorrow. She can take twenty or so people, sounds all right, thought you'd like the idea. See you in a tick!

– A what?

He had hung up. A tick!

Why this sudden persistent focus on me? Plenty of women at this party were single, extremely attractive and a lot more glamorous.

While I took a long bath, I tried to collect my thoughts. Was Christopher attractive? Not really. Coarse hands and teeth in need of care had made a first, negative impression. His blatantly self-satisfied attitude did not improve it. On the other hand, I liked the voice and had not often met so disarmingly transparent an Englishman. But then, Christopher had been raised in Sicily and schooled (where else?) at Eton. He had worked in America for some years and now lived in Zurich.

Had he been a stranger on a train, I might have noticed a well-dressed and obviously well-bred man in his fifties absorbed by such noble callings as money-making and perhaps golf. Be that as it may, this was no train and my spirits were high as I dressed.

The dinner was lovely. Others made the jokes, Christopher laughed at them. Even though his favourite topic of conversation was himself, he knew how to make others feel important. Later on, we went to a bar. Bad dancers are lousy lovers. Was this an issue? Not yet. For the time being, a few vodkas had greatly mellowed him.

The boat trip next day was fabulous. He made everyone feel good at over-ostentatious expense. I was flattered by his keen interest. At some point he took me aside.

– Let's leave tomorrow.

– Leave? Tomorrow? What about Brian's barbecue and . . .

– Forget it. We need time together and I have little to spare.

– But Chris – sorry, Christopher – I rented a car, booked a flight . . . Besides, frankly . . .

– I have a surprise on the way to Zurich. You can fly back from there. Everything will be taken care of, including your car.

It is not my habit to desert parties I am invited to and elope with strangers for whom I have no strong feelings.

– I want to know you better, Aleana. The truth is I wish I had years ago. Don't worry! Life's too short.

That was no scoop. Now: apart from determination, I am easily seduced by the words 'don't worry'. I have been doing too much of that for too long. An only child, a rebellious adolescent, an independent woman, I had begun to crave, however vehement my denial of it, for the stability my over-emotional character kept sabotaging. For the 'one day he'll come along, the man I love, and he'll be big and strong . . . ' evergreen come true. For protection and, with a little luck, love. I looked around. Other than Christopher, everybody was getting plastered, including myself.

The long and short of it is that I left with him the next day.

Things moved fast from there.

The stopover on the way to Zurich was magic – and speedy, like everything with Christopher. In the Provençal *relais-château* that seemed hanging from the clouds, we had lunch on a terrace, just the two of us, a scene out of a romantic movie. It transpired he had booked all the tables – most considerate.

We started talking about what, ironically, most future couples talk about: the past. We also broached other subjects. He was articulate and knowledgeable. I was impressed. He laughed at my jokes, which is always pleasant.

What followed was predictable. In the vast room, the curtains of which had conveniently been drawn, he peeled off my clothes and threw me on the four-poster bed. We explored our skins and sensitivities. They fitted. Having ascertained that, Christopher ordered dinner, asked practical questions, was not displeased with the answers and proceeded pulling out his agenda for making plans. These spanned over half a lifetime, short of a wedding date.

– Marriage is a luxury these days, he informed me, hinting at the generosity of what he was contemplating.

Christopher obviously did not like to waste time. Next day we met his 'closest friends' – whom he had not called for a years – and raced up to Zurich at tremendous speed in his supersonic car.

I was dazzled, puzzled, a little dizzy and very amused.

*   *   *

If happiness is peace, it lasted three months. If happiness is peace, the absence of passion only enhances it. That was fine with me – precisely perhaps because of being out of character.

I had had my share of elation and disillusion in recent years. Christopher gave me the much longed-for feeling of having 'reached port'. This would by no means be a harbour bustling and hissing with demons or delights. There would be no tough guys sneaking down dark alleys, no lascivious smiles above high heels nor clandestine goods or precious stones on ships whose blowing sirens recalled forlorn places. No. This would be the harbour to anchor in. It would feel safe, it would be fine.

We thereafter spent every second week together, either as guests of some friends of his, or on business trips all over the place. He was an investment banker; president, chairman and (need I say?) owner.

It was actually very interesting, a little too frantic perhaps, but Christopher knew how to make up for that by creating romantic stopovers, Provence-style. When we were together, he took care of everything, decided what I should wear, made lists of what I should do or visit, and so on. I rather liked that, strange at it may seem. He made a woman feel a woman. Not least, at night. Generally speaking, his vitality swept one along, which was marvellous.

Early December I called Christopher one evening, sobbing.

A television deal on which I had been working hard fell through. My car was stolen. It rained cats and dogs. I felt feverish, despondent and lonely, in need of support. None was forthcoming. Instead, he embarked on a stern speech about the importance of pulling oneself together and how he'd had to learn it the hard way. When he started on about life not being a party and some such crap, I hung up.

Foolish me, I thought. I should have known better.

Flowers for no reason, a kind word or a gentle embrace were not his wont. Patience with frailty, or tolerance of failure was not in Christopher's chords either. Moreover, and in a diffuse way, I had sensed his disappointment at my lack of single-minded ambition. I was by no means an over-achiever as he was. Whenever he talked with awe about someone – a rare occurrence – those were the character traits he praised. Oh well, I thought, he has other qualities, and so do I. We would have more time in two weeks, during the Christmas holidays.

Yet, at the very back of my mind, a query was curling into a pregnant question mark: was he a man to rely but not to lean on?

I swept it aside and concentrated on rescuing the deal, an important one as it concerned a contract for a five-episode film, with me as co-scriptwriter. The very day we finally signed – it was December the seventeenth, as I vividly remember – I received an e-mail.

Christopher announced point blank that he could not cope with my expectations, had doubts about his own, concluded we should go our separate ways before ugly dramas tore us apart. All of it 'in a tick'. '*Ciao bella*' was the affront he offered at the end.

I couldn't believe it.

What dramas? Drama was a recurrent word in his vocabulary and obviously an omnipresent spectre in his mind. A man married for altogether thirty years, who raised children, ran and created companies, now a bank, could not possibly discard the need for adjustment in relationships – or could he?

For once, I did not allow pain to crush me. I just sat there, playing 'in the eye of the hurricane', a game I should have invented long ago, and forced rationality to sweep emotions aside: was Christopher yet another fake toughie of the sort I seem doomed to attract and who ultimately vampires on one's strength? No (argued my mind). He had to be different (pleaded my heart)!

In any case, being a pretty determined person myself, I was not going – or able – to shrug a nonchalant shoulder. A notorious recidivist at sentimental mutiny, I was intent on not ducking yet again. We had gone too far not to go to the end, if the end was inevitable. As we had planned and agreed, I was going to Davos three days later.

This is what I e-mailed back. No more. He merely answered that a car would be waiting for me at the airport.

We did eventually spend those two weeks together, but without the slightest intimacy. Entrenched behind the cruellest of barricades, silence, without a clue or a reproach, Christopher left me to myself. He was frostily kind but distant. Constantly surrounded by others, we acted in a 'civilized' way. Whether his friends liking me pleased or irritated him I do not know.

At night, the show was over. He slept like a log while I tossed and turned, praying for a release from anxiety, wondering what to do.

Timing! Did I get it terribly wrong just when it seemed so right?

All I knew is how it felt. Horrendous. It was as if, gazing on to a bright and boundless horizon, an invisible hand abruptly pulled down the blind. I felt homesick. Unfortunately I had always imagined home as the man who, wherever or anywhere, would represent its very roof.

Either Christopher was not this man, or else I had lost a home.

Unpacking, I had placed our keys in the same drawer and our

CDs on the same shelf. Some hours later, his keys and CDs had been removed. Why did I not leave right there and then?

Had he only taken the risk of words! Had he only been willing to let go! Expressing the roots of mixed feelings could have defused much subsequent damage. Did I discourage him? Had I not mastered enough self-control to stick to the unfailing formula of seduction: flatter, entertain and expect nothing?

It was torture.

One day, having lunch in a mountain hut during which I amplified my booze consumption, Christopher told a lady seated next to him that, all things considered, he did not feel ready to change a life so flawlessly organized around his work, his sons and sports. And by the way, he would move to Geneva and take over the flat of a bachelor friend of his. (Geneva! Not a lucky place as far as relationships were concerned.) I was meant to overhear, and did. Still too much 'bruised' by Johanna, an ex-girlfriend who had met another man and become engaged soon thereafter, he could not face commitment. Besides, women craved for things he did not have.

Oh?

Later, I steadied my nerves in a bar, drinking some herbal tea for a change. The same lady we had lunch with, Chloë, walked in. Women have an instinct for hidden pain, and obviously I wasn't the first casualty she had seen in such a shambles.

– Good gracious! You look terrible! she exclaimed upliftingly.

– That's because you've never seen me sober before!

– Ha ha! I must remember that line, she laughed. How are you?

– Disappointed. Disgusted. Disenchanted. You name it.

– May I give you a piece of advice?

– What kind? I said, rising a suspicious eyebrow.

– To act fresh and unnatural, that sort of thing.

– In a situation like this, Chloë? Thanks.

– Honey, if you can't fake, you can't fly. Why should a hunter chase what follows him? Would Christopher pursue a red-eyed wingless bird?

– Yeah. I must have thought it interesting to fall into a trap set up by my own delusions. The stuff of tragedy and farce.

– Stop being negative.

– I'm tired of not understanding.

– It's not complicated. Showing your feelings, their being hurt and you insecure, means he feels uncomfortable. Just what men most resent.

– Really! So what do they like? Bitches? Snakes? Masochists?

– Wake up, Aleana. Men are *simple*. Women analyse, wonder, doubt. We all too readily endorse responsibility; feel guilty, believe relationships require intelligent, imaginative solutions. Meanwhile, what does a man think? Nothing. Or else, something totally unrelated to our concerns.

– So what *do* they want? I snickered (or sniffed, can't remember).

– In essence, no problems.

– Women that neither ask nor answer questions?

– Could be. Look honey . . .

While gulping down a double Scotch, she looked radiant, albeit confused for a split second. She took a deep breath and examined her empty glass.

– Let me tell you this: disappointment is universal. George, the man I have been living with for ten years, is in Mexico right now, with a girlfriend and . . . *their* bloody four-year-old child I had no idea existed.

– You're kidding! Why didn't you tell me before instead of letting me bask in self-pity?

– To make us both feel even worse? she snapped ironically. It took seeing his suitcases packed – with a framed picture of us, *and of them* inside, would you believe – to believe it myself.

– Christ. How can you act so cool?

– The way I act is merely a way of not drowning.

– *Chapeau*. You fooled me.

– Anyone can!

– . . .

– Sorry! I didn't mean it as it sounded . . .

I couldn't help laughing. Finally she ordered another drink and relaxed. Whatever people say about alcohol, it does help on occasion.

– Darling, this is no wonderland and you are no Alice. This is real life. Forgive the cliché, but you're a handsome woman with a family, friends and talent, or so I heard. I am okay too. And there we stand, like lost puppies in some backyard. Being older than you, let me remind you that love is *not* condemned to the electric bed! It's our sentimental behaviour that's ill adjusted. That being said, choosers can't be losers.

A line *I* had to remember.

– What are you going to do?

– Redecorate the flat. It's cheaper than a shrink, and those darlings know all about gay islands, ha ha, in exotic places. I need a holiday.

– And George? What will you do when he gets back?

– Smile, threaten suicide and pack. All very Egyptian.

– To achieve what?

– Getting even. Or getting him back.

– But you lost all respect for him! I exclaimed. He insulted your pride, trampled your feelings . . . What on earth can you expect?

– A decision. On my conditions.

– It sounds like . . . I don't know, like a power struggle . . . depressing . . .

– Peace is the outcome of wars.

– What do you think I should do? I asked after a pause.

– Give Christopher time. He isn't my favourite person by any means, but he had to harden by force of circumstance. Don't forget his father died when he was very young so he had to become his own source of authority in many ways.

– Too late for that. And please, don't expand on the theory that nothing, strictly nothing decisive happens in a human being's life after the age of six.

Chloë had one of those figures that wobble merrily.

– Three. But since you mention it, I wonder . . . Christopher always pursued two aims at the same time. Women are like nuts to him: he finds it impossible to open one without crushing another. To tell you the truth, I think you should fuck off (or him, ha ha) and forget the bastard . . .

– Not easy.

– Pull yourself together, darling. Oh my gosh, I must run! Lovely to talk to you! By-yyyye!

I remained at the bar feeling none the better for this marathon conversation. Words! Perhaps I just wasn't gifted for this gamble called love. Crochet might be a safer alternative.

Long before Christmas, some 'girlfriends who meant well' had put me on my guard. The bottom line was the 'treat them mean to keep then keen' platitude. If Christopher thought he was an irresistible seducer, he could dream again. A lot of women did not particularly like him, as I had discovered long before Davos. 'Too much of a bully', in their opinion. I ignored all that talk, just as I refuse to regard love as a battlefield requiring tactics as Chloë, another voice in the chorus, seemed to advocate.

Time had come for a retreat into absence. The harm was done and I dreaded the sequels. Robbed of my sense of humour, I was becoming a burden and a bore. It would have taken but one comforting word, one gentle squeeze, to help a little. But that hope was chimerical. Exposure to more? No way.

I left Davos determined to wrap myself in dignified silence and wait. A holiday to me, right then, was loneliness at home.

*   *   *

In the taxi that took me to the airport, my nerves cracked, my heart crumbled, my composure disintegrated. That very morning Christopher had jumped into his skiing suit without a shave and bolted out of the hotel room.

In the plane, I fell asleep, at long last.

Home: some strange energy made me unpack within minutes, make scrambled eggs and open a bottle of whisky, which I loathe. But there was no wine in the fridge, so what the hell? In spite of the soothing silence, I kept pacing my flat perfumed by scented candles, in blazing anger, half-mumbling, half-thundering. After a while, hopelessly frustrated, I decided to put pen to paper.

I hesitated between Vivaldi and Brazilian jazz, opted for the latter, then dithered between 'Dear Chris' and 'You cruel bastard' but discarded both.

How dare you? Three months ago you wanted us to get married. It wasn't exactly a proposal: it was a shopping list! There you sat, enumerating reasons. I was the right age. Wanted no children. Spoke four languages. Had class and charm and sex appeal (I quote you). We had mutual friends and similar backgrounds. In short, I was the missing piece in the puzzle of your impeccably organized life. A winner in his fifties could do with a wife, or should I say, an *apanage* like me. Then, the denial of it all. Per e-mail! Frightfully modern!

The damage is deep. I fought a lost battle. Persuading you we should give chance a last chance and spend Christmas together as we had planned was undignified. But the e-mail that shattered all I had foolishly mistaken as being genuine could not be the end of it, I thought. Being close could perhaps revive or rescue the feelings we had shared. I was mistaken and should have realized it. You had drawn back, closed up, and panicked. Couldn't you have said so, instead of using standard sentences such as, 'I can't offer what you deserve,' yet agreeing to give 'it' a tick to sort 'things' out?

What the fuck happened? Whatever is was, it must have occurred between the first weekend of December, which we spent together in harmony, and that e-mail dated December the seventeenth.

(Another sip of whisky, another cigarette.)

Was I in love myself? I think so, wanted to, desperate to believe it. For three months, you gave me stability and serenity. I hoped that trust and tenderness would come with time, given patience. Meanwhile, it felt damn good to feel desired. I liked and admired you. I loved the rituals of togetherness. The daily phone call. Looking forwards to sharing 'prime times'. When your caring turned into control thirst, I did not mind. My weaknesses should have reassured you, come to think of it.

(A squint in the mirror. Not a pretty sight.)

Anyway. I left London in reverse gear, arrived insecure and behaved off- balance. You had a crush on me, and now I am the smitten one. I hang on to anger as to a rope with which I would otherwise strangle no one but myself.

Silence is one hell of a lethal weapon. You used and abused it. I feel manipulated and humiliated. I don't deserve being treated as the cause of your emotional panic: faced with what, if I may ask? With getting what you no longer want? With my giving too naïvely what you promised too fast? Not performing that classical dance of seduction I've never been good at, one demure step forwards, two feline steps backwards, I was too easy to get – unless the consequences were too difficult to assume.

A dream come true is a reality to face. You turned away without warning.

(*More disgusting whisky and funkier music.*)

Who the hell do you think you are anyway? Do you seriously believe that women in general, and me – beautiful, loving me! – in particular, are craving to catch a fish (your astrological sign, to worsen matters) like you? Who wants to live with a man not particularly funny in a soporific place like Zurich?

Becoming stepmother to two pompous brats, as a bonus? Making fast love on Saturdays?

Sex! That frail bridge was bound to crumble when other forms of communication fail. You prefer obstacles to shortcuts.

To expect love from a man with your background was nutty in the first place. A product of the English stiff-upper-lip cult, you were taught to shelter under a sentimental parasol, passion or even warmth regarded as dangerous flaws. Ever so keen to be in the limelight without risking exposure, you listen to other's problems with a seemingly concerned but actually conceited ear. You have been there, seen it all, and twice. You are past caring. So civilized, isn't it, old boy?

(*Wow.*)

Distance being safer than dialogue, you beat all records on the highways of life with frigid haste. Expensive toys tame your fears, boost your ego, but in the end, you are a supine son of a gun. Financial takeovers and Lamborghinis allow you to escape from private issues. You can run, and you sure can hide. But for how long, I wonder? A crash is on the way, be it only because vulnerability isn't on your books. That would require the kind of guts you don't have. Living on the defensive, you need to feel threatened. Like most men, courage outside a battlefield or a racing track is not your forte. Hence, you fight invented wars, unable to cope with peace, and shield behind that impeccable façade varnished by inherited titles and flashy cash.

(*Had to open windows. It was too hot. Or I was, more likely.*)

You Etonian cowboys worship competition but cannot handle confrontation. Getting violent is easier than getting verbal. Fencing is a technique easier to acquire than the handling of words. Swords scar nothing but the surface whereas emotions stab from within. Hang-ups, hangovers . . .

'Bruised by rejection', are you? Your wife throws you out, a girlfriend turns you down and you attribute it all to female fickleness? Not altogether convincing. I have come to doubt whether the wounds you pretend are unhealed were deep in the first place. Yet in a way, you need motherly reassurance, patting on the cheek, sycophantic adulation.

Anyway, rejection seems to be a leitmotiv in your life! And now you make me pay for it? A bit harsh, isn't it? Back-pedalling on the bumpy grounds of the future fits the pattern. But don't you dare accusing me of being merely human!

Bref. I blame you for the damage you inflicted with open eyes and a hermetic heart. I blame you for making me feel a failure at inspiring lasting love and desire. For losing my sense of humour as well as my confidence. For my dwindling weight, the visible symptom of my injured appetite for life. For the sadness that poisons my mind. For not being able to laugh and forget . . . *Ciao bello*.

(*An exhausted blank.*)

Having expulsed my indignation and deflated emotions, doubts about my own self were not long in taking over. It was all very well to belabour Christopher. What about me?

I recalled our laughs, our making love or just snuggling, lazy afternoons playing Scrabble, long and easy conversations, our holding hands in a theatre, after which he had entrusted me with a secret that required utter trust. I really did believe that our relationship could have paved a sunny street. Otherwise would I have fought for what I still had faith in?

But there was another point of view: his. Why would a man barricaded against emotions want to cope with an oversensitive woman unable to control her own? Was what I most needed tenderness, the one thing he could not offer? And vice versa? Invertedly, Christopher wanted someone uncomplicated by his side. Someone content with un-erotic sex, small talk, a predictable and comfortable life. Not me.

If feminine women, in his ideal scenario, were meant to give the cue to the main protagonists or decorate the stage of plays in which men held the leading roles, that would have been fine by me. Secondary parts are indispensable to get the argument moving. What I did expect was respect.

Did I lack respect myself? I blamed myself for being intolerant with his habit of not letting you forget his title or wealth, or putting the tip of his ten fingers together when speaking about his self, or rushing around replacing books or ashtrays in their proper place: details, all things considered. Showing icy severity towards the failings of others while being blatantly self-complacent was another matter.

However: what the hell did I want? More than everything? It

was time to grow up. To accept what we all know: no one person in the world can fulfil one's expectations. There are friends and books and music to turn to. There is the awareness of one's luck when being healthy and privileged. The plight and misery of others, not in deepest darkest Africa but round every corner, should constantly put things back into perspective. They don't, of course.

All too often, the longing to love and be loved in return fades all else out. Love isn't blind; it is an obsessive focus. Love is monomaniac.

Was I not overreacting to wounded pride? Had I not myself reduced him to a sum of qualities matching my ideal? He also was the right age. His children were young enough to have a good time with, yet old enough not to be around. My father would have been pleased about the name, and money seldom harms. Christopher might not have been a ball of fun but he certainly wasn't boring. My fantasy could have balanced his conventionality. Love without passion is said to have fair chances of lasting.

But then again: would I have been happy with a man who, with rigid discipline, stuck to an unbending routine? During the week – fine, perfectly understandable. Yet weekends were equally submitted to a mechanism as precise as a cuckoo clock. During the winter and since twenty years, skiing in Davos. During the summer, horseback riding on the same estate in Scotland. The remaining months demanded improvisation, something irritating to Christopher. Was it a coincidence that he declared eternal love in September and buried it in December?

Were his reading in church at Brian's wedding and the power he gave to words like 'endurance', 'faith', 'wholeness' or 'love' nothing but skilful elocution? Had it all been sanctimonious smoke?

I tore the letter apart and pruned it to a few words: 'What a shame, what a waste, what a pity. Toodloo.'

*   *   *

Convalescing from the ghastly two weeks in Davos took time. But, as usual, the passing of it did the trick. Gradually other concerns helped alleviate the pain, and professional gratification ironed out the turmoil.

In February (not the fourteenth), I finally sent Christopher a thank you letter. After all, he had been very generous. Its off-handedness pleased me. He never responded. I heard, through Chloë, that he was a little vexed, having expected more tantrums.

Shortly before Easter, I was in Paris to meet some producers. This trip gave me the chance to see a cosmetician I had known for some time. It had been a treat to have my skin cleaned and my body massaged by sweet Annie. I felt pretty well, or should I say, reasonably pretty and quite well again? Pangs of melancholy still drilled my stomach and heart on occasions. Having memories with Christopher in Paris, I was much on guard. Time is a devious magician.

As I stood in front of the reception desk waiting for the bill, I sensed a pair of insistent eyes drilling into my back. Annie mean-while was not mincing her words:

– It's all right putting all on the account of a *chagrin d'amour*, but you must take better care of yourself. No man is worth jeopardizing your complexion for!

I listened distractedly. My awareness of the woman behind me was putting me ill at ease. She stood up when Annie disappeared to fetch her *potions magiques*.

– Sorry, but isn't your name Aleana?

– It is.

– It may sound strange, but I would like to invite you for a drink.

– Thank you very much, but . . .

– Weren't you a girlfriend of Christopher's?

Quite tall, quite slim, dressed in a Burberry coat, wrapped in a Burberry shawl, a Burberry handbag hanging over her shoulder, she might have stepped out of a Burberry ad portraying the typical English rose on a shoot outside her family's stately home. She had a good-natured, self-possessed manner, rather fine features with frank if unremarkable eyes. For some reason, I thought she must have very neat, small handwriting, slanted to the left. All in all, she seemed nice. We must have been more or less the same age. Her face vaguely reminded me of someone. I was glad Annie had put make-up on mine. I smiled.

– Sorry, but who are you?

– My name is Johanna. Chloë, who happens to be a good friend of mine and a fan of yours, showed me a photograph of the New Year's Eve party in Davos, which is how I recognized you.

I was startled and could not help looking at her carefully, nor thinking she was rather plain. So this was Johanna? The girl Christopher could not forget? The *killer lady* who had so 'bruised' him he could not get over it?

Annie now handed me a parcel the size of which expressed her opinion about my condition louder than words. The bill was no smaller.

Johanna addressed her with firmness:

– I shall be half an hour. Let's make my treatment that much shorter. Thanks.

Here was a no-nonsense woman.

We went to an Italian restaurant near by, which was empty at this late stage of the afternoon. The bar, thank God, was open. I needed a drink. So did Johanna, who continued to observe me closely.

– I heard you were good-looking. No exaggeration.

– Thanks.

– Still living in London?

– You seem well informed!

She gulped her drink in no time, making herself even more likeable before declaring:

– I'm exhausted. And quite pregnant too.

Not knowing what to say, I said nothing.

– Aleana, you should be aware of certain things. Chloë was in a terrible state when you left Davos. She told me how miserable you felt and that what made it worse was your not understanding why Chris behaved as a cad.

– That pretty much sums it up. She was a great support.

– That's not how she felt, poor thing. To cut a long story short, when I bumped into you by chance, I thought I might be able to . . . help.

– Help? Really?

Notwithstanding her good intentions, Johanna was about to get on my already frayed nerves. She must have read my heart, for her tone changed abruptly.

– You wasted your time with Chris.

No kidding. Had I not heard all this before?

– Listen, Aleana. He probably told you that having loved and lost me he could not face commitment. Right?

– He did. Indirectly.

– I imagine he also said it would take him ages to recover and he could therefore hardly be blamed for not being able to recipro-cate love, meet expectations and so on. Right?

– Yes.

– And people, I suppose, told you I treated him like shit?

– Indeed.

This was getting jazzy.

– Well. What he said was bollocks but what people said was correct. I did treat him with the polite contempt he bestows on most women, including you, I take it. But worse – forgive me – on girls like my sister. While divorcing, he met my sister who was then twenty-five. He seduced her, got her used to a grand lifestyle, made her heart wild and her character tame. Then he dumped her on the grounds that she was too young. The blunt truth is that he no longer needed her. She had fulfilled *his* purpose, done her time, uplifted his battered spirits which, *owh passage,* allowed him to get back at his wife, who had filed the divorce.

The story, frankly, did not move me to tears. The girl must have had a good time, she was young and by the looks of it, had a solid home to fall back on and a tough sister as an ally.

– You met Chris last September, exactly a year after I did. He was desperate for someone who fitted his life. *Natuarellman* he got frantic because I didn't care, which is when he decided he had.

– What?

– Fallen in love. Things do not happen to Christopher. He decides them to happen. 'In a tick,' as he would say.

Johanna's constant falling, presumably because of my own accent, into a French requiring a fair knowledge of English to make sense of it, was funny. She asked for another two glasses of wine and some cigarettes.

– I stopped smoking. That's the easy bit. Not to start again is *ley problayme*.

We had a lot in common, it seemed.

– The man I'd been in love with for years was married. Marriage on the rocks cannot be broken, hence I didn't break his. Thing is, married men are clock teasers. Promises postponed, and so on. Time went by, nothing changed, except for my wanting children. I'm thirty-seven. Something had to happen for *Henrey* – he is from Bordeaux – to make a move. I used Chris to trigger off jealousy.

Now here really was something new. Why did she call him Chris, not Christopher, as I had been exhorted to do?

– I went to Davos, as you did, for Christmas. During Easter, we went to Chile, helicopter skiing. I never pretended to be in love. That, more than anything, turned him on. After the trip he somehow found out about *Henrey*. He went mad. Not mad with anger, as you'd expect – mad with determination. His having an adversary was a further challenge. It also reassured him. At least, he could put my lack of interest down to something that did not directly involve his ego.

– But Johanna . . .

– I know; one shouldn't use people, *evtceyterah*. Well, I had no pangs about it, considering the antecedent with my sister. It took her ages to get over the guy, so it seemed okay to get back at him. What isn't fair is that he should have used you to get back at me.

– What on earth do you mean?

– Just what I said.

If what Johanna said was true, it was sickening.

– I understand you write fiction?

– Well . . . I try.

– I'm a computer scientist, but I won't bore you with details. Just to say I'm the matter-of-fact type of chick.

That put me back in my place. Grown-ups were boxing in other categories.

– The only thing that made my whole scheme bearable was sex. With Chris it was great.

Suddenly I regretted having followed Johanna. Certain information I would rather ignore. She took me unawares by shooting her next question:

– Did you have a double bed in Davos?

– No. Twin beds. By then, frankly, it didn't matter.

– How wrong you are! chuckled Johanna. Too bad. If something could have mended the broken pieces, it was a large bed. Chris is easy to handle once you understand where the steering wheel is . . . *too m'ah comprée.*

I thought of women in general. Many are witches. Others, on the contrary, display immediate solidarity with their gender. Johanna belonged to the latter sort. She inspired mixed feelings, eroticism not among them. Her hands contrasted with her frail figure and fine features. Her teeth were none too white.

Uncannily following my train of thoughts, she pursued:

– The almost frantic attraction I exercised over Chris was pretty narcissistic. When he looked at me, he looked into a mirror. Being furiously pleased with himself, he found me irresistible!

– You're a good storyteller, I laughed heartily.

– I might tell a story well but am hopeless at inventing one. Point is we could easily have been brother and sister, to judge by looks, perhaps mentally too. Facts and figures being what Chris best understands, we had a common language. Budgets, profits, probabilities, that kind of thing.

Although she made me feel like a schoolgirl, I liked her. Johanna was a cool cat, and a lively one.

– So what happened? Did Henri get alarmed?

– Not a bit. My scheme backfired. Instead of getting jealous, he was relieved. Oh, he did love me . . . But men prefer the problems they know to the hypothetical, should they be even worse. That's a fact.

– Might he not have been hurt? I ventured.

– *Henreyyyy?* No chance, to my dismay.

– I meant . . . Christopher. Weren't you a bit, just a bit, attached to him?

– Of course I was! Still am. We had a wonderful time together, mainly skiing. I behaved like 'one of the boys', you know? A bit of a giggle, a quickie, the good sort. But after a while there was no longer any reason to hang out with him. The truth is I got bored. Bored with his monotonous phone calls that invariably followed the same sequence: weather conditions, earnings, planning and timetables. I was also bored with his acting so old for his age. On top of it, I couldn't suppress the vulgar thought that, having invested six months of his time and money, he demanded a profitable return. Be that as it may, the bottom line was that I just didn't love him.

– When did you break off for good?

– Oh . . . soon after the trip to Chile.

– No regrets? Ever?

– No, Aleana. For a while, I missed his taking over and taking care, but I didn't love the man, really.

A lump formed in my throat. That goddamn sadness again. Johanna sensed it.

– You know, the best is always to come, as the saying goes. Exactly a year ago, I couldn't sleep without pills or stay at home without television, stereo and Internet switched on simultaneously. I had lost the man I loved, and sent the one claiming to love me to hell. I wanted a family and was giving up faith in myself, in the future, in relationships and what not. Well, soon thereafter I met *l'hoam dey mah veey.* It was instantaneous – and it's for *reeeeeal*!

Her eyes became dreamy. Was she a softie underneath it all?

– Tim rented a villa in the South of France and Chris accepted an invitation to visit He never showed up, of course. Called to say he was about to get engaged too, sounding triumphant.

– In September?

– That's right.

Johanna paused, threw me a sharp look and fell silent. Her beauty treatment was by now reduced to sancerre and Marlboros.

– May I ask you something?

– Of course.

– What made you so nuts about Chris? I mean . . . you seem kind of fragile. Why love a guy who can't give affection, doesn't read fiction and talks like the *Herald Tribune*? I'd imagine you with an architect, a writer or something. Dryly rational minds like Chris can't cope with artistic personalities. According to Chloë, you aren't even a fanatic skier. I'm not a very tactful person, but I'm curious, I must admit.

– All of which answers your question.

– You got me lost there.

I had to pull myself together to go on.

– I have known few strong men who know what they want and whom nothing stops from getting it. I admired that. His kindness and concern, even though more practical than anything, reassured me. I could not grasp him, which I found intriguing. His being predictable in many circumstances was offset by his reacting in unexpected ways, most of which were disconcerting or hurtful. Then . . . the sex.

– See? That's what he's all about.

– I wouldn't say so. There was more, Johanna.

– Don't fool yourself: he married once for the convention, a second time to be mothered, and would or will marry again for the trophy. He believes that caring is paying. His kindness is heartless, honey.

What more was there to talk about? I could well imagine Chris, as she called him, fascinated and led on by her – perhaps, among other reasons, because she would not call him Christopher: she was strong. There was one last thing.

– Do you know what happened in December?

– What do you mean?

I hesitated. This was really crying out for help to someone who had unwittingly been co-responsible for my distress.

– Well. What still tortures me is not understanding why, having sneaked into my bathroom on the first of December to measure my ring size, made plans for a chalet and future trips that same afternoon, he then recklessly torpedoed everything a couple of weeks later. Without warning, without explanation. Per e-mail, for heaven's sake! All right, I had irritated him on the phone the previous night. Yet in all fairness, that can't have been it. I stormed my memory to the limit but to no avail. Do you have any idea what happened?

She looked me very straight in the eye.

– I told you he wasn't worth it.

This was leading nowhere. I was tired. Where was my coat?

– Ideas, no. But what I do know is that I married Tim on Saturday, December the sixteenth, and Chris read about it in the press. Whether it was my getting married or my not telling him that drove him ballistic, *meestare*. Point being, I received an e-mail too. Ferocious it was!

How could I have been stupid or conceited enough not to realize that Davos was a delusion bound to end in disaster? While I was hanging on to a ghost, what was Christopher doing? Hatching his revenge.

– I see.

Johanna burst out laughing. There were both malice and fondness in that cascading laugh.

In fact I saw nothing at all any more, except a big black hole. At the bottom of it a fool: me.

Suddenly, I also started laughing. Uncontrollably. Neither of us could stop. Tears – or was it years? – ran down our cheeks.

Charly's Château, Easter 2002

PART TWO

Can't Lie Any More

The Week After

14–21 June

The plane, having successfully slalomed through lightning, landed safely at Geneva.

My taxi driver was very talkative: he was French. Predictably he started commenting on the weather, bemoaning how it was like everything else in Switzerland: hybrid.

– It's neither continental, nor Atlantic, nor Mediterranean, it's a little of each – the image reflecting this pluri-ethnic, multi-cultural country.

– What made you want to live here?

– My wife wanted to. There were too many burglaries in Normandy. Little did we know how difficult the paperwork would be, *la vache!* ['holy cow!'] Can you believe it that Geneva alone counts as many civil servants per capita as Paris? Twenty-five thousand for approximately six hundred thousand inhabitants! That's forty per cent more than in Zurich. A nightmare.

Traffic was bumper to bumper. It was raining torrentially.

– Really? I thought everything was swift and efficient here.

– What you see can be misleading. I'll give you an example: there are more sects in Switzerland than in any other European country. Extremes meet. Just as it can be tropical and polar, mysticism and Calvinism seem to feed on themselves. This is a country of either speculation or certitudes, divided by mental walls, as the topography is by mountains. On the other hand, the civic sense has similarities with the American. Nobody is more patriotic than a recently naturalized Swiss! Over there, they run around with a flag in one hand and a Budweiser in the other; here, with a flag and a chequebook. The victory of pragmatism over refinement is another example. Anyway . . . I'll be glad to go on a holiday tomorrow.

– To Normandy?

– No, the weather is lousy there too. We have a house in the Provence.

When we eventually arrived and he showed me the amount on the metre, I could see how he could afford three residences. Taxi drivers in Geneva must be taxed on wealth.

The girl in whose house I stayed not being there, I went to bed early.

Friday, I had lunch with Christopher, 'The Man Who Most Hurt My Pride'. He looked his part, the distinguished British finance wizard – and very attractive too.

We had seen each other occasionally since breaking up seven years before, but always on rather impersonal terms. Since I had used his office to print out what I have so far written I gave him a copy. Perusing the pages, he immediately understood where I had been and why. Over lunch, we talked like old friends, free from the coolness he usually displays, though he kept true to his telegraphese style. His present dilemma is whether to stay in Geneva or return to London, where his family and girlfriend live.

– How is London nowadays? Haven't been there for many years.

– Tremendously changed. People incredibly laid back. In the City, average age thirty, no striped suits, no ties. They arrive on bikes, change in the office. Earn bloody loads. Expensive? Freaking understatement. Real-estate agencies look like jewellery shops. Amazing. At the same time, lots of small businesses. Smallest of all, shoe-polishers, flower or newspaper stands, take-aways and so on. You'd think you're in Malaysia. But the infra-structure, a bloody nightmare. Do you know that more deaths have been caused by train collisions in the UK than in India over the past five years?

After this unusually long sentence, Christopher gulped down a whole glass of wine.

– What does your girlfriend do?

– A bloody shrink, he retorted, his periwinkle eyes teasing me.

I nearly choked. Matter-of-fact Christopher, not inclined to intimacies, with a psychiatrist? I took the kind of conscious breath the *Pankafit* teacher had demonstrated to ask:

– Had my drinking something to do with your falling in and out of love with me at such a dazzling pace?

– Would have dealt with that. Wanted to marry you, remember?

– Was it . . . er . . . that ex-girlfriend you still couldn't get over – Joan . . . ?

– Johanna? You kidding? She was an accident about to happen, and so she did, convinced she was irresistible. Whole family a mess, mind you.

Christopher fleetingly showed his worst profile, not physically speaking.

– No, he said, it was my sons.

– They disliked me?

– Yes.

I had tossed and turned a thousand reasons in my mind, but the obvious one never crossed it. The dislike was cordially reciprocated: his teenaged sons were, at the time, of a conceit beyond imagination. The intent with which they cloned their father in every minute detail was grotesque, or certainly overdone for kids their age. Towards me they were polite and stiff, Eton-style. Be that as it may, I should have asked earlier. *Now*, I understood. Robin would never have married me had his daughters not adored me and encouraged it.

We parted with a bear-hug. An hour later, Christopher called to say that I could stay at his flat whenever I wished in Geneva; his way of admitting he had enjoyed our luncheon, without actually saying it. I was glad. It's reassuring to leave a favourable last impression. I wasn't sure we would see each other again. Some leaves are better left turned.

Walking past cafés in which I used to read the papers with a glass (or two, or three?) of wine, I felt unmoved. In the evening, I was invited to some friends, took along a few cans of vegetable juice and had the best of times.

On Saturday, 'The Man Who Most Wounded My Heart' (and pseudo-protagonist of my short story 'Double') came to fetch me – an hour late, as Hugo would be.

We drove up to a picturesque medieval village in the mountains, halfway to Gstaad. There he had a business meeting with one of his partners. I took a long walk with the latter's wife, Hugo's secretary in 'my time'. On the way back, it poured with rain again. Hugo invited me home for dinner; his brother was coming too. It seemed a good idea, and it was: I learnt a lot, even though no food was produced as he had forgotten to instruct his house-keeper. We ended up eating yogurts.

His brother, who looks very much like Hugo – green eyes, enticing smile, huge amounts of black hair – is an intellectual artist, the trendy and tiresome type. He started lecturing about recent discoveries made on the basis of the double helix, and ended by saying that, there being no such thing as race, racism was an aberration, all the more so considering that humans shared almost ninety-nine per cent of their genetic heritage with chimpanzees, most vexing for the latter. For some reason, conversation drifted to cancer. I knew Hugo had overcome a rare cancer. What I had *not* known was that the cancer was rampant while we were together; it was diagnosed much later, and called by then for 'microsurgery in a big way', as he proudly emphasized.

Meaning: he had been ill during the three years we more or less lived together. Also meaning: *now* I understood his constant tiredness and our rather a-sexual relationship.

Hugo went on to describe the severe depression following his illness. It corresponded to everything Dottore M had told me: blurred vision, no concentration, trouble executing the simplest tasks. But it was the medical aspect which most interested him:

– Over the last twenty years, research has concentrated on the low level of a pair of neuro-transmitters, serotonin and noradrenalin. Recent studies have established beyond doubt that nervous cells and cerebral circuits can be permanently damaged by too long an exposure to stress, or even by one single traumatic experience, such as cancer. In these cases, it is vulnerability or over-reactions to stress that must be treated: antidepressants are not adequate. To tell a depressed person, 'Come on, show a little more good will and energy!' is useless: he cannot do it. A Copernican revolution is under way in cerebral knowledge. With time, our brain becomes a photograph of the life we've been leading: genetics as ominous aren't as we believed.

I found this a relief. The idea of being predetermined by, and therefore the puppet of, a mathematical chain in the DNA had always disturbed me, and more so these past weeks.

– Neurosurgery, he continued, can nowadays interfere with and improve these cells and circuits. But so can therapy. By changing thinking patterns, by taming emotionality, by redesigning one's affective landscape, it can enhance the mind's control over brain and body. Emotional intelligence is something that can be acquired. Buddhist monks, when submitted to instrumental tests at Wisconsin University, have shown astonishing mutations in the frontal cortex area, these leading from regular and specific meditation techniques which make it more receptive to well-being. Mental training can modify the brain to the point of enabling its creation of new synapses, that is, new connections between its cells.

He seemed to have become quite an authority on the subject.

– Now listen! A group of volunteers in an experiment at Harvard Medical School was asked *to play* a simple tune on a piano for two hours a day during two weeks. Another group was asked *to think of playing* the same tune for the same amount of time. In both groups, the cerebral area corresponding to finger movements had been 'colonized' in equal measure. The implications are . . . mind-boggling. They clearly demonstrate that thinking in a positive way does influence mental mechanisms – and also behaviour patterns. Healing can be a self-generated discipline. While pain cannot be avoided in life, our reactions to it can be steered. Is happiness an art after all?

– There is no art without serenity, declared the brother, quite categorically. All the mythology about *les poètes maudits* and the tormented, boozy artist is a sham. Creation is a long and tedious struggle requiring blood and sweat. Above all, it requires the peace of mind allowing insight or distance, alterations or nuances. Progress in art usually moves towards simplicity. Is inspiration more fertile under the ascendancy of drugs, alcohol or pain? Depends. But true creation crystallizes as work begins, and to work well, you need all your wits.

– I couldn't agree more, I said.

Corrections and re-corrections demand more time and effort than the writing itself. In the clinic, I had written without dictionaries, which would make rewriting an even longer process.

– And I'm also convinced happiness is an art, unless you content yourself with a state of steady satisfaction coupled with an absence of longing, which I couldn't.

The brother asked if he could stay overnight. His car had been making strange noises and the rain was torrential again.

– Of course, said Hugo. Why don't you stay too? he suggested to me. I can take you back tomorrow.

Geneva was thirty kilometres away, and I knew he wasn't keen on night driving either. So I answered:

– Why not?

A dangerous answer, as I have often and belatedly realized. The brother gone to bed, we stayed up another hour or so in Hugo's chaotic study. Suddenly he announced:

– I want to confess something to you I've never told any woman before.

What he described pertained to his youth and I do not wish to transcribe it. I am no adept of sadomasochism, bondage group exchanges and other permutations of the like. However, while I must admit I was fascinated and appalled in equal measure, his adroitly trumpeted so-called confessions left me dubitative. In the past, Hugo had lied not only by omission but also, and mostly, by exaggeration. Was he doing so now? As suspicion does not leave room for the 'suspension of disbelief' a raconteur requires, the degree of trust was equally missing.

If Hugo noticed it, he gave no sign of minding. His conception of truth has always been ecstatic rather then exact. Fabrication to him enhances rather than distorts reality. In fact he despises accuracy as an accountant's concern. Yet, as I well knew, he was a manipulative, not exactly machiavellian, but Florentine all the same in his fool-and-rule expertise.

– I'm as selfish as a saint, he sighed complacently.

Nice, but borrowed from Jules Renard . . . The gullible audience I had provided him with fifteen years before had been multiply bitten and was no longer shy. Being sober, I remained silent, baffled to see that whereas even stones aren't immune to mutation, Hugo was. He had not changed an iota, at least not in his lifestyle, aloofness or mental arabesques. Nor had he lost his hair or his jocularity. The astonishing thing being that, when you tell people they're exactly the same, they usually feel flattered. Oh well. My thoughts then drifted Lugano, where I had relearnt the risk of veracity. In short, I was in no mood for games and Hugo's loquaciousness seemed hollow. Was the king naked? Not yet, but just in case I stood up abruptly, tossed a curt good night and went to the guest bedroom. He could fantasize in his; I locked my door.

The room, which had been an attic, was lovely. The windows were wide open. Outside, the bleating of sheep, the mooing of cows and the croaking of frogs, which normally I find an exasperating racket, conveyed tranquillity. I marinated in a scented bath. I found a good book. The bed was vast and the sheets crisp linen. None of this, however, prevented me from feeling ill at ease. Was it because of Hugo's epically erotic tales? Or was it because, deep inside, I could not be comfortable under the roof of 'The Man Who Most Wounded My Heart'? Unexpected vibrations in between my legs woke me in the middle of the night. It was a dream, and one I did not enjoy. Be that as it may, I was glad to wake up next morning and depart – alone. I sauntered to the nearby station, feeling gay (no pun!).

It was now Sunday and sunny. My plane to Palma being due to leave at six in the evening, I did as tourists do: a round-trip of the lake on one of its old-fashioned steamers. It was thoroughly enjoyable. The art therapist would have remarked how boats represented an escape and how this could be no arbitrary decision . . .

At the airport, as often happens in Geneva, I met someone I knew and became a part of a small piece of anthology in the annals of absurd conversation.

Peter is charming but none too bright a fellow. He is Swiss and looks it: a jovial face on a robust body. I had known him and his successive wives for over thirty years. He seemed uncharacteristically agitated.

– Aleana *chérie*! What a surprise! Good to see you.

And without transition:

– When have you seen Tracy last?

– Tracy? In Madrid, I think.

He pulled out a leather-bound notebook, on the cover his initials embossed in gold.

– When? Was it a weekend? Where was she staying?

– It was shortly before Christmas, November perhaps. Why? What's this about?

– Don't confuse me with questions!

– Hey, Peter, are you nuts? Why not ask me for a video recording? I laughed. Frankly, should I remember what day or time it was?

– Was she alone?

– No.

– Ah, thought so, he boomed. Who was the bastard?

– Your dog.

Realizing I was going to prove no copious source of information, he divulged that he was conducting a private investigation with his divorce in view. The notebook was bursting at the seams. Poor Tracy – well, not for long. I remembered she was Californian.

– My lawyer and I are at the bar. Our flight is delayed. Care to join us?

I was reminded of a similar conversation . . . in Barcelona airport! Circles do close.

As soon as I saw who his lawyer was, I had to repress another laugh. If opposites attract each other, here was a blatant example. Maître B was a pompous pedant, incapable of punctuating his speech without Latin aphorisms or maxims too subtle for the minds of common mortals. It was rumoured that he had won many cases by unnerving judges to such an extent that they would yield to his requests just to shut him up.

Naturally Maître B mistook my smile for gleeful delight.

– Enchanted to see you again, my dear (he had forgotten my name, for sure). Just the other day, I was thinking of your thorough catalogue inventory, years ago, and your delicacy in handling books.

– How is your collection doing?

He really did have the most beautiful first and rare editions, especially of travel books, that I had ever seen in private hands. Making that catalogue had been a fabulous assignment.

– 'Developing' is the word you were looking for. Anyway – don't mention it! This morning I walked into my study and there stood my son. *Horresco referens!* What do you think he was wearing?

Nothing but tattoos was my guess. The boy had been just another brat as far I was concerned.

– Pyjamas! Can you *believe* it? *Pyjamas* in my study! An insult to human thought and spiritual achievement! I told him so in no uncertain terms. How can one show such *laissez-faire* and *laissez-aller* in front of objects deserving the highest marks of respect and veneration? Intolerable.

I pictured this tenor of the bar reading in bed, wearing a black tie. He again mistook my smile for undivided acquiescence, but on observing Peter, his expression turned into dismay.

— What *are* you doing?

– Answering a text message.

– I can see that.

– So why do you ask?

Generally speaking, Peter was the sort of character who would reply, if asked whether he had been to *The Marriage of Figaro*, 'I sent flowers instead.' In this instance, he had scored a modest point. Maître B proceeded to expound his views on the matter to me, casting eyes and hands heavenwards.

– Cellular telephones, a calamity! And that insipid code people write their messages in, another curse of our times. Is there any better demonstration for the impoverishment of language, for the disintegration of verbal communication, for spiritual desolation? An SMS is the SOS of shipwrecked souls. It is to conversation what 'pass the salt' is to eroticism: the end. I have banished women from my affective forum who would utter such trivia.

What were they supposed to do? Ask for salt by sending an SMS across the table? Funnily enough, at that very moment his own mobile rang. A man of principle, he snapped it shut within seconds.

– Where was I? Ah yes. Well. *Medice, cura te ipsum!*

– How's work?

– The law is finally admitting that human beings are *not* born equal. A small step for man, a big step for mankind. It fills me with blithe confidence, dear Aleana. (It was me who had forgotten he never forgets a name.) Much time has been wasted on utopia.

Africans would not have been amused to hear that. Peter was.

– Having a good time?

– Just a bit of small talk. Splendid nevertheless.

– Do you know you are talking to a star? Peter mellifluously asked me.

– I do.

– The star system is another plague, thundered the man who was notoriously one of its big profiteers.

– I love stars, but only at dark and . . . horizont-ally, squeaked Peter.

Tracy was not only Californian, but had been a small-time actress. She would certainly claim to have given up her promising career for eternal love: perjury.

– How's your investigation getting along? I mischievously asked.

– Very confusing, most confusing . . . She's been seen by everyone everywhere with everybody, except at home with me.

– Abandonment of domicile, muttered Maître B. Better than adultery.

– What do you mean? snapped Peter.

– Legally speaking.

– Is that so? he inquired, vividly interested.

– *Magister dixit!* I said, collecting my bags. Good luck.

On Monday I woke up late. It was good to be home.

I went out to buy food, light bulbs and things like that, and was welcomed back by the local shopkeepers cheerfully. Living in Palma old town is like living in a village. Our distaste for the hordes of unkempt tourists who lumber through the streets during holidays creates bonds; familiarity reinforces them. When not shockingly rude, the *Majorquins* are an expansive care-free people.

The last few days passed in a flash. It is Thursday. Exactly three weeks after I walked into the clinic at Lugano. Having done little except rewriting and swimming, I have little to report, other than noticeable changes:

- I seem to ask for permission all the time, regarding the silliest things.
- I don't feel like watching TV.
- I talk less (my husband is thrilled).
- I am as distracted as before, but more methodical.
- My eyesight has dwindled and so has my weight. I lost three kilos in five days after leaving the place, and do my best to put them back on, but have no appetite. It's steaming hot here.
- I have not returned most calls.

- I am less quick-silvered, but less mercurial too.
- I drive like a grandmother, prudent and scatter-brained. The first time I took my car, in an unusual zero point zero state, another driver crashed into mine: an ambulance. I laughed. My fault: I had stopped at an orange light! I then headed for a beach club where I had spent most of nine summers and thrice took a wrong turn.
- My sleep is profound and undisturbed. I seem to need less of it. When I wake up, no black thoughts invade me.
- My handwriting is more linear, and less impulsive.
- What I now drink costs half of what I spent before; but I smoke more.
- All in all, I am more patient, and much more *serene*. It's a wonderful feeling!

. . . Until this morning.

Hoping to speak to my father, I talked to my mother on the phone. Her 'transmit only' switch must have been blinking furiously. She started complaining about health and heat, made some nasty remarks about my father's twin sister (she just cannot help it; why such vindictiveness? I poignantly ask myself), made a short story about a raincoat long, and finally, drawing breath, asked what I do – not how I am. I told her I had been very busy writing.

– Writing what?

– Oh, a sort of collage of impressions, feelings, thoughts . . .

– Well, well! Is that a good idea? What you write is *always* so pessimistic!

Needless to say, this upset me – but not emotionally. How could she say that? Above all, why? She has read nothing at all other than my book reviews and satirical columns. (Later, I remembered my letter after Christmas.)

– What about looking for a job?

– I'm doing that.

I explained two possibilities, and why it wasn't easy. I should have used my fetish Scotch tape to muzzle my mouth.

A few hours later, the mobile rang. I know my father's voice and knew at once he was upset.

– What's the matter, Daddy?

– Nothing much . . . I just wanted to call back. And, oh, by the way . . . er . . .

– . . . ?

– . . . If you prefer, we can postpone our trip to Constantinople, it's not . . .

– Why? Why should we? I exclaimed, taken aback and alarmed.

– Well . . . your mother tells me you can't find a job because of our trip in September, and so, you know . . . er . . .

I protested vehemently and told him I had only said I would start whatever it may be in October, as I was to spend the first half of September with Robin and his children, the second with him. That was all. I made chit-chat a little longer and could hear his relieved smile when we said goodbye.

She had done it again! Again she had turned, twisted and distorted words in order to insert the knife at the right place! How sour can a person be?

I wasn't upset any more; I was flaming incensed. For the first time in exactly three weeks, I felt the announced 'craving'. Just as well I was in the car. For her eightieth birthday, I would send my mother eighty pounds of sugar, each packet wrapped and ribboned, plus a note saying: 'For Mother Sweetest. Something for coating acidity.'

But . . . *Sustine et abstine!* My brand-new philosophy.

This same afternoon, I had an appointment with the psychiatrist recommended by a psychologist friend. Dr Juan asked me 'what the problem seems to be'. Jesus, I lamented mutely, the whole freaking story from scratch? He *said* I had undergone a detox cure for body and mind, that I was there because a follow-up had been adamantly advised.

He reacted with exuberance to my abridged version.

– I love these cases, he said with much gesturing. They are so very interesting and gratifying for a doctor, because as long as depression and addiction aren't excessively interactive, the end of the tunnel is always round one of the many corners we can map out!

– Fantastic, I waved back.

Having pieced together all I could sum up, my mind went blank. He made all sorts of compliments about how lucid and self-critical I was, above all how articulate, but then also seemed to run out of anything more to say. He pulled out his prescription pad and announced that I needed chemical help to resist temptation in my present surroundings.

– Fifty micrograms of Revia will safely get you through the next few weeks, the most tricky ones, I warn you. It blocks the centres of pleasure associated with substance intake. One every morning, Aleana, without fail, understood?

It sounded like the equivalent of methadone for alcoholics, and what the hell, I need all the help I can get, so I agreed and left, relieved of quite some money and promising to consult him once a week. He almost crushed my phalanges in his enthusiastic farewell handshake.

The following day, off to Munich and Robin – at last. Alleluia!

Then, a week in Corsica, invited by friends whose main occupations are drinking lots and eating well. Sitting next to our host at dinner is like inhaling pure phosgene. The only amusing thing, when stone sober in that kind of situation, is noticing who is imaginative and who isn't. The latter repeat the same things in the same way, whereas the former invent successive, increasingly elaborated versions of the story in hand.

Anyway, I was not afraid, since my adorable husband would stand by me. However: *Sublata causa, tollitur effectus?* The effect has disappeared; but has the cause?

Time will tell – and so might I, in the final chapter of this 'collage'.

Two Months Later

1 August
Full moon, full circle

Where does the line between serenity and indifference meander? I worry less about a staggering amount of things. 'So whats' seem to be taking over. That *does* worry me – a little.

Our flight to Corsica, for instance, was one big hassle that left me totally unfazed. The plane was delayed, diverted to Milan, then delayed again, all of which had a *déjà vu* flavour for me. Robin was wildly irritated, not least by my passivity. I just sat around with the vacant look of a fish, and one no longer drinking. Even mineral water had to be paid for on this airline. What a crowd! Flying may well become cheaper than staying home, but if the present trend continues, people will soon travel in pyjamas and be asked to vacuum before disembarking.

The days in that house appeared interminable. Robin was happy, since our hosts are old friends of his. They were constantly nagging at each other, the sea was icy, and I caught a kidney infection. As well as being ill, I was bored. Unless it was I who was no longer fun? I discarded the thought, but not the realization that, sober, you become too critical to be puerile, which, most of the time, is the indispensable ingredient of fun. Anyway: what did my 'adorable husband' do? He urged me to sip a glass or two, arguing it was a wholly different story from binging on a bottle or three. We had a fight. Everybody went out boating and I . . . drank.

My mind started claiming that, shivering and freezing as I was, alcohol would warm me up. Besides, the cunning traitor elaborated, it was not my fault but Robin's. He let me down: he would be sorry for it. As it turned out, I was the one who paid, and a high price too for half a bottle of Martini bianco. I was sick as hell, provoked another fight, and after an atrocious night of guilt and anger, swore never to succumb again. So far I haven't. Footnote: *Don't think you're strong, because you're not.*

Back in Palma, I recovered my calm and my rhythm. Writing is my buoy.

Lisa spent one week with me. Like a pallid sun, she no longer radiates warmth. Although our addictions were different, she is the one who seems to have a permanent hangover. Whereas abstinence cleared my brain, hers seems to have crash-landed in some desert, close by an absurd phone booth. She spent most of her time sending text messages to a wimpy lunatic whom she despises but chases, be it to furnish time or fulfil other needs. Money seems to have changed hands . . . 'The story of my life,' she dryly remarked. Other than that, when not shopping she gossiped about people she no longer sees and anecdotes dredged up from some foggy past. The result was dismal, not to say Felliniesque. After an existence of grabbing everything, Lisa ended up with nothing and feels bereft (here I paraphrase a line in a funky book, *Prozac Nation*, which is a scream, in the double sense of the word).

Yesterday, I called Dottore M.

Kiki has killed herself. She previously told her room-mate in hospital that she had lacerated her legs and arms for years as an acceptable crescendo in pain for the sole purpose of one day not being afraid to cut her throat.

This time, she enrolled in a 'suicide club' on the Internet, a sinister forum for collective intentional death. By her side was the book *A Complete Manual to Suicide* by Wataru Tsurumi, which sold over a million copies in the past few years. Great Britain has converted itself into the third country (after Japan and South Korea) with the highest number of victims from such 'clubs'. Dottore M would volunteer no information about any other patients, hence I called Gilda.

She told me the 'Cat Hater' responds so well to his 'cartoon therapy' that even his allergy to feline hair is cured. 'His mother had a stroke,' she offered as a cryptic explanation, probably with a smile. The barmy American set fire to some curtains to catch attention, and was thrown out. The 'Music Monk' continues to recede towards childhood; he has replaced his pipe with lollipops. Gilda worships him, as she craves for a hermetic shelter of her own. Whereas I stopped being a kid too soon and Giuseppe wants to revert to being one, Gilda never snapped out of being exactly that.

Tonia and I talk at least twice a week. She, Marco and I promised to meet in Rome at the end of the month. Crans-Montana is no longer on: his wife Fiori, counselled by some vulture lawyer, has claimed guardianship over his possessions. He doesn't fight back. Tonia says he *cannot manage to bother*. She also says she feels utterly helpless, as therapists often do when faced with their private life (her words).

I had two more sessions with the Palma shrink, Dr Juan. The other day he did not hide his displeasure at my having cancelled our previous Tuesday's rendezvous. Dr Juan seemed extremely agitated, all traces of enthusiasm vanished.

– I have read the chapters you dropped off after our last conversation, and I very much disagree with the advice given you in Lugano.

– Oh?

The chapters he referred to were the ones in which I tell about my mother and our relationship. I waited. He started pacing the room, rather athletically I thought. In his early forties, he was obviously a fitness freak.

– Yes. Avoiding a mother is no solution. Not only because it is unfair, but because all it does is postpone further pain. What you must do is rise to a meta-semantic level . . . Yes, it sounds abstruse, but all it means is that you must learn to be twice removed, and address her in the third person of your mind's grammar. Treat her as stranger deserving respect.

What Dr Juan said made a lot of sense to me.

– You have spent most of your life believing you had to 'save' your father. Let him be his own lord and master. What you can do for him now is help him maintain peace – or the appearance thereof. You are too absolute, Aleana, and when the price means cutting back on honesty and letting the weaker win, then you must pay it. You have nothing to lose and your mother has her pride to win back. Give her the chance. Call it her birthday gift.

As I reflected on that, Dr Juan gazed out of the window. A remnant of anger contracted my stomach. However feeble, it made me emphatic.

– You know, Dr Juan, what therapy in Lugano helped me to do was 'take the garbage to the can'. I might be able to do as you suggest, but again – at meta or alpha level – my mother and I are unlikely to stand, think or feel on the same platform. *She chose* to miss the train, supposing she ever consulted a timetable other than her biological clock. Do you know, she spent years comparing Adlerian with Jungian theories without it ever occurring to her that she just *might* need therapy herself? Can you imagine that she contemplated, instead, becoming a therapist?

At that point I was getting agitated. I felt the start of an urge to scratch the backs of my knees. Resisting it compounded my state.

– Do you think, Dr Juan, that my mother ever wrote me a letter in the last twenty or more years? A real letter? One in which she might have ever so slightly *hinted* at being prepared to *contemplate* the *remote* possibility that our conflictive tension could just *possibly* have had *something* to do with her own attitude? No.

I leaned back in my comfortable armchair, feeling uncomfortable. My heartbeat was becoming arythmic. Dr Juan sat down.

– Listen. You write on a computer and therefore know about defragmentation. Pause, shut your eyes, block your brain and defragment. Try.

– How? I asked in that pleading voice of mine I so detest.

– Try to see things from your mother's angle.

– I can't.

– You could.

– Her perspective is too vertical, mine is too horizontal. She looks at things and people from above.

– This is frequent with people locked in vanity.

– Maybe. But how can I relate to that? There is no possible level at which we can meet. If she moves from her position, the scaffolding she has so intricately chiselled to remain at the top crumbles, meaning that she falls.

– Who said so?

He had me where he wanted – cornered. Even physically, the symptoms of mental claustrophobia were gaining ground. He resumed with a smile:

– Listen, Aleana, put it this way: your mother wants to be right? Acquiesce with her, regardless of your opinions. She is old and you have little time left to mend what is amendable, knowing that nothing coming from you will ever be good enough for her. You have to live with that.

– You're right, and I know it, but . . . how do you think I felt over the many years when my mother retracted from a simple kiss on the cheek with unconcealed aversion? How do you *presume* it made me *feel*?

Vibrant melancholy filled the air in a palpable way.

– My sister had a similar problem with our mother. She is now plagued by remorse. The strong one must give in. To be right at the wrong moment is useless.

Turning back to me, he sighed.

– You are the stronger one in this case, but other than that, extremely fragile. How's abstinence going?

Not really caring, I spilt the beans and confessed I had started drinking again, very moderately and only extremely diluted Camparis, but still: the mechanism was reactivated and kicking, and if not in full swing, then none the less on its familiar spin. The mental wheel of a hard day's work deserving reward, tiredness requiring a boost, occasional nervousness needing a soothing balm or an unpleasant task courage was turning in slow motion,

yet inexorably turning. Dr Juan observed me closely. He decided
to believe what I said.

– Do you take the Revia pills as prescribed?

– No. I stopped. They produced such dryness in my mouth that
I couldn't even drive without sucking on a water bottle, then
needed to go to the loo at the most inconvenient times and
places. Sorry.

This very much upset the doctor, who returned to his pacing
and gesticulating.

– Right. We will not see each other next week . . .

I cringed like a kid about to be punished.

– . . . we shall see each other tomorrow, same time, sharp.

My relief must have been childish too, for he patted me on the
shoulder, showed me to the door and almost – or was I imagining
things – slammed it behind me.

I walked to the cathedral and sat on a shaded bench. Closing my
eyes and shutting off my brain was just as impossible as refraining
from scratching the back of my knee, soon to be an open wound,
I anticipated, remembering previous allergy fits – all of them
related to my mother in one way or another. To treat her politely,
call her the French *vous*, was probably the smartest thing, for
she had become a stranger I did owe impersonal respect to.

I probably don't know her; I only know what she showed and
said, and how both reverberated upon my highly strung hypersensitivity. Respect! Due respect! Why should a parent not feel
compelled to show respect, too, as a crash course in further
education? There was a time when I would sob, muttering, 'Why
is she so rude to me, why doesn't she wish me well, why?' It wasn't
long ago. On that bench, I felt tired of thinking about my mother,
writing about her, talking about her. Enough of headaches and
tears and allergy fits. I was empty of feelings all of a sudden. I
really had had enough.

Back home, I retrieved the famous pills and studied the leaflet.
Hm . . .

Strong stuff, also recommended for drug abstinence, especially opiates. The list of contraindications and possible side-effects seemed endless. I threw the box away and took a decision.

The next day, I would tell Dr Juan something I had not told the psychiatrists in Lugano. For one thing, I had quelled and obfuscated it in my own memory, and for another, I wanted to concentrate on the urgent problem in hand, or so I justified making the omission. In truth, I had repressed this period of my life because of its leading to my first marriage, which I am ashamed of.

About fifteen years ago, I sublet the basement of my Parisian duplex flat to an Englishman I had met in Geneva in the eighties. He had been a successful gallery owner and lived in great pomp. He was handsome, extremely witty, and had been very kind to mutual friends in distress. He resurfaced in Paris, his *grand seigneur* style unchanged, and we spent a wonderful, interesting evening together. When Paul mentioned he needed to spend a few months in Paris and somewhere to stay, I told him about the possibility at my place, making no mystery of my shortage of cash. The deal was done, and started out under the best of auspices. He was courteous, mostly out and about, or fun to be with when around. After a while I did begin to wonder what he was up to from overhearing quizzical phone calls and witnessing his strange habits and moments of elation. At first I gave it little thought, the art world being what it is and people being weird anyway. One night I gave a dinner party, during which he shone with his knowledge and anecdotes. He kept taking guests aside to show off his 'quarters', which I found odd but touching, their being nothing special. Whoever re-emerged always appeared to have become much more animated. Finally, it clicked: coke.

I had taken the odd line on occasions, of course. I say 'of course' because the eighties were the cocaine decade *par excellence*. I did so again that night, and then on many more nights, and soon during the daytime too. The following four months were highly productive. In cooperation with a professional ghost writer, who became an eager participant in our increasingly humdrum snorting, I worked on a documentary about two Lebanese crooks. The period also coincided with the appearance on the scene of Cedric, the creep I was to marry. He and Paul became great pals – not surprisingly, both being con-men. The latter had turned out to be still a dealer, but no longer of art; Cedric, living and moving under the false name of Trickson (hint, hint), was dealing in all sorts of commodities (not drugs), posing as an art dealer commissioned by some Hong Kong tycoon (who I doubt existed) who (naturally) wished to remain anonymous.

What was I, brainy me, thinking of? A lot. I never stopped, my brain being greatly accelerated and stimulated by the stuff. I wrote at high speed, and well. I discovered that most of my friends were not averse to accepting a line as a recreational kick. We laughed enormously. I never exaggerated my consumption, at first, and fooled myself into believing I had a ringside seat in a convenient case-study: researching con men could be done at home! Actually, outlaws have always intrigued me. Their psychological profile, as I see it, encompasses fascinating common denominators (I am referring to the colourful, white-collar type, not to sleazy back-street thieves):

- They are artists with the minds of chess players, having to reinvent their personae constantly and adapt to carefully calculated risks. Their thinking patterns are diagonal as opposed to cursive most of the time, and by necessity one move and one square ahead of others. The conjunction of fantasy and logic underlies 'crook-craft'.
- Moving step by step is to them like going nowhere. They need to move in leaps and bounds, further and faster beyond the limitations imposed by the law. Acrobatic balancing acts are their forte. Audacity replaces morality in their scale of values, as temerity equals merit.
- There is a lot of pride involved in outsmarting the system. It

is the system they despise, not the laws. They do respect the latter, but only to pulverize them. Breaking the rules calls for a reconfiguration of the game. Accusing them of cheating is the most vexing insult you can throw at outlaws. To them forgery, for instance, is no crime; it's a tool.

- They crave recognition at the fringe of conventional frameworks. Actors on the stage of their oversized, inflated egos, they perform to monopolize the limelight, a private mirror. Their souls are very photosensitive!
- Their Florentine trades requiring unrelenting vigilance, their brains are on constant alert but their spirits free: that's their charm and power.
- Crisis management and solution finding is based on anticipation. Hence, imagination and creativity, the prerequisites of their *modus operandi*, are overdeveloped and hyperactive.
- Outlaws are methodically irresponsible in their dealings with others, not caring a hoot about feelings or losses they inflict on them. They are manipulative liars and ultimately mythomaniacs, believing in what they have faked.
- They prefer evanescence to substance, improvisation to habits, masks to faces. (They seldom wear sunglasses though: looking harmless is of the essence.)
- Their brains, unrelentingly vigilant, are on constant alert, but their spirits are free: that's their charm and power – to me at least.

Do they really want to beat the system? In the long run, no. They are far too clever not to realize that theirs is an ephemeral chimera, and they gamble while they can. My guess is that ultimately it's all about winning a bet.

What was it made *The Thomas Crown Affair* as much of a cult film as *Bonnie and Clyde*, and why do church-going housewives and lawn-mowing accountants find such anti-heroes awesome? Why was Orson Welles ultimately celebrated for his cruel radio spoof of an alien attack in the 1930s? Why has the Briggs train robbery stamped itself on our collective memory? Why is Napoleon, a flop in military and sexual tactics, remembered only for his visionary strategy? How, closer to our grotesque showbiz culture, did a bimbo called Hilton become an icon?

Because we lack guts, and admire people bigger than life. Because what can't be forgotten is more magnanimously forgiven, money and/or success being a help. Because dreams are catalysts. Because the panache mobilized to outfox the system captures the imagination while laws straightjacket it.

Anyway . . . There I was, getting on with the documentary script and sweeping my forebodings to the back of my mind. Naturally, I realized this coke business was no good and sheltering a dealer tantamount to plain madness. But the situation seemed contained, for I stuck to my health routine, going to the gym, eating normally, drinking next to no booze and spending a few early nights a week in bed, reading or catching up on sleep. Cedric, Paul and I went out on most other nights, with or without friends, and in all fairness both taught me a lot about art; they really mastered their subject.

Towards the end of the third month, this precarious equilibrium was significantly shaken by the arrival of Paul's American girlfriend, Kate, an authentic nutcase – and junkie. By then, busy with interviews instead of writing, I was out a lot and did not realize the subtle ways in which Paul and Kate were taking over, first in terms of space (she didn't like the basement), then of time (they would often wake up when I returned home in the late afternoon, would spread out upstairs and invite her chums). Kate had studied paediatrics in Paris, and knew lots of people: too many. The trouble was, I liked her. Besides being mad, she was interesting, loads of fun and pretty. So were her friends. (It's amazing how many addicts have a medical background.)

In short, cocaine was now a constant fixture and I started to take a line at mid morning to get going. The flat became a meeting point where curtains were drawn most of the time as a protection against unwelcome observation. The scenario, in retrospect, was not unlike that in Polanski's film *The Tenant*. Sometimes I became so fed up with the buzzing activity at home that I went to sleep at Cedric's place. There it was alcohol that flowed galore. In those days, it wasn't my problem, at least excessive drinking wasn't, but still . . . this lifestyle was taking its toll. I felt on my knees with exhaustion, and exasperation too, but directed my anger at myself (my mother couldn't be blamed, could she!).

One day, I found Kate in a panicky state. Paul had collapsed in a restaurant and been taken to emergency at a hospital. She was loaded. More than her boyfriend's health – this had apparently happened before – it was the possibility of a police investigation that worried her. Now I panicked too. We went through his belongings and found a staggering amount of white powder. First thing we did was to take a generous amount to gather our wits. Needless to say, the reverse happened and we became even more frantic. I called Cedric, in tears and at the end of my tether. He came over, helped himself to a large amount as well but kept his head and took over. Three hours later, Kate and Paul's suitcases had been packed and transported to a small hotel; the basement cleaned and sprayed with disinfectant; and I put to bed with a hot-water bottle. As usual, my nerves had hit my stomach. What Cedric did with all that coke I never asked . . .

I had had enough. I wanted my peace back. When, a few days later, Cedric suggested we fly to Florida together for the wedding of some friends of his, I accepted in haste with relief .

There was more snorting going on there, but my body rejected the mere thought of it. I was upset and off balance after four such hectic months. On the other hand, I played tennis daily during the first week, and read a lot. How and when Cedric came up with the idea of us getting married, as an arrangement convenient to him for family reasons (probably bullshit), and with the proviso we would divorce as soon as he had cleared some inheritance matters, remains hazy to this day. What I do know is that I found the prospect *funny*, which goes to show how seriously my mind was altered by the substance – even though, strangely enough, I didn't have the slightest withdrawal symptoms then or the slightest craving since. Our entourage found it funny too (we were the most implausible couple, from an aesthetic viewpoint to begin with) and basically, we all giggled and drank ourselves through the farcical procedures.

All of this had happened within forty-eight hours, for in Florida all you need is identity and cash. The awakening was bitter. It came all at once, the infamous 'day after'. I realized what I had done as if slapped in the face. The worst bit was having to announce this folly to my parents. I have *never* been so embarrassed in my life. They reacted with a composure I shall never be able to thank them enough for. I guess that their friendship with Cedric's father helped to cushion the shock, but still . . . Christ. When they insisted on throwing a celebration party upon our return, I thought I would die. At the party, I nearly did.

It took me six years to nail him down, living under yet another false name, and I had to pay for the divorce.

Since it is naked sincerity I pay for nowadays, I wondered what Dr Juan would make of this latest instalment.

– It figures, he shrugged, alarmingly less agitated than on the previous day.

– What do you mean? I winced.

– Is it safe to assume that the drug triggered off over-intellectual reactions rather than emotional responses?

He was right. I was stunned.

– Very safe, I contritely answered.

He was right. Why had I never thought of that? My feelings, sentimental and physical, had been numbed. Those who claimed cocaine arouses one sexually made me sneeze with ironic detach-ment. All I wanted, after a few lines, was talk, talk and talk: the antidote to eroticism, right? Or else, for lack of an acoustic audience, write, write and write. In both instances, sharing was a remote concern. Whereas under the influence of alcohol, diffuse pain or anger are misdirected at whomever has the misfortune to be around, under the influence of cocaine one succumbs to the urge of monologues easily deteriorating into 'duelogues'. One speaks the truth, and nothing but. In other words, from being communicative it becomes isolating. A refrain from I forgot what song could be coke's slogan: 'Oh babe, don't let me go, I'm getting high on feeling low.' Being alone, however, does not hurt, since you do not feel pain.

There was another problem. Unlike the 'morning after' syndrome with alcohol, cocaine hits you with total recall unless you mix both things, which I didn't. Most of my co-snorters did, and had forgotten most of what happened on waking up. This was just as well – or probably worse. The extraordinary thing for a worrier like me was the devil-may-careness that kept me afloat. This, I have to admit, *was* a kick.

Jumping into my train of thoughts, Dr Juan resumed:

– I'll spare you a lecture about the effects of cocaine and derivates on the nervous system. You are a well-informed person. But again, I depart from the conclusions of your Lugano therapists. Genetic depression is *not* your problem. The depressed episodes you were lately confronted with were mainly due to a hormonal disruption; generally and mostly, to the consequences of addiction. You are an addict, Aleana, but now listen carefully: whereas you appear surprised you did not become hooked on coke, I am not. It isn't as much alcohol or chemicals to which you are addicted as to *excess*. You are the type of person who races ahead at random, but only with her two hands firmly on the steering-wheel. Am I right?

He was. I have always opted for driving with caution, eyes riveted on the road ahead, even if it means not consulting a map on the passenger seat, thus wasting time and getting lost. Quite a metaphor.

– If rich, you'd be a shopping or a charity freak; if interested in the Internet, you'd not surf but jet on it; if wild about sex, you'd be a nymphomaniac. The reactive chains are roughly the same.

Mediocrity is the primary spectre looming in your mind. Everything else represents a crutch for limping away from it. That's the real problem. You must *accept* it. Etymologically, 'acceptance' means: *the act* of understanding.

I waited for him to continue. He waited too. Finally I said:

– I don't know what to say. I think I have spent too much energy rewinding, exposing, listening, analysing, wondering, writing – about me, me and me. I think I need a long break. If what I am told is true, if exteriorizing turmoil, anger and so on does deliver you from it, I think it's overindulged in, and done. Yesterday, after leaving your practice, I sat near the cathedral, with no feeling left at all. The sensation of breathing oxygen took up all the space. Do you believe all this thinking might have created space to be filled anew?

– Definitely. Leave as much as you can behind. Didn't you use the expression 'taking the garbage to the can' yesterday? Well, you have, and in a creative way. Now *let it rest*.

He fiddled with some papers and stood up.

– Listen. Having given it much thought, I am convinced that the next step for you is hypnotherapy. At the stage you have reached everything else is counter-productive. Here is the address of Dr Altamira. I have taken the liberty of arranging for an appointment next Monday. Trust me – and above all, trust her. She will know how to help at the core.

Laconically he added:

– You're attaching. Take attentive care of yourself, and keep in touch.

No smile, no handshake.

I spent the weekend on the beach perusing magazines, or not doing even that. I savoured my cerebral blank, more relaxed than in a million years, or so it seemed. As a bonus I have, by sheer chance, discovered a swimming technique which releases minuscule orgasms, like fireflies in the dark. I am very pleased.

I have also been offered a job. It consists of opening the

Balearic Islands to such products from Lombardy as prosciutto, parmesan, pasta and the like. Friends who dropped by the other day (and left in a hurry when told there was no booze around) derived much merriment from picturing me roaming the streets hauling loins of pork. One of them remembered me as the baroness who had created a travel magazine for Amex; another reminded me of my period as a journalist; a third reminisced about my selling palatial villas. All three hooted with derision at this new prospect. 'And now our dear countess is going to peddle ham and cheese, is she?' they teased.

So what? A job provides an income, money buys time, and I need both to forge a **pink** future. I still believe in the improbable, and in the over-quoted wisdom of the Corinthian: 'In a word, there are three things that last forever: faith, hope and love; but the greatest of them all is love.'

Having devoted inordinate thought to the past, time had come to make Robin and the future my first priorities again.

A Dream is a Lie Come True

Doctora Marisol Altamira was a plump and jovial woman in her sixties. One thing she had in common with Dr Juan was an iron handshake; otherwise, she was soft-spoken. They must have discussed my case, for she put it in a nutshell.

– We are going to aim for moderation. It can be learned by training.

I raised a sceptical eyebrow.

– Do you consider yourself an addict right now? she asked, evidently not one to beat about the bush.

– That's hard to answer. People who stop drinking abusively call themselves alcoholics for life, don't they? For the moment, I am a 'writaholic'. I know I *must* start working on my new project as soon as I finish the present book, otherwise . . . well.

– Quite.

– Aside from keeping my demons in check, it makes me happy.

– Good.

She changed chairs from the other side of her imposing desk and sat next to me.

– Traditionally defined in terms of psychoactive substances which cross the blood–brain barrier, dependency has come to include gambling, food, sex, pornography, computers, work, exercise, etcetera. As an extension, abatement of abuse is no longer seen solely as the cure of addiction but of behavioural disorders too. In the contemporary view, the trend is to acknowledge the possibility that the hypothalamus creates peptides in the brain that equal or exceed the effect of chemicals. When addicted gamblers or junkies satisfy their craving, endorphins are produced and released within the brain, reinforcing the individual's positive associations with their behaviour. This is precisely the link I shall intend to sever.

She looked at me with appropriately piercing eyes.

– What do you know about hypnosis?

– Not much. I have heard about the sleep temples and mystery religions of ancient Greco-Roman society, and the parallels drawn between hypnotism and the trance-inducing rituals in pre-literate societies. I vaguely remember reading about Émile Coué's methods, apparently similar to hypnosis and a very popular form of self-help in the crazy twenties. Other than that . . . the typical stuff about one's concentrating intensely on a regularly oscillating object, being lulled by a voice, falling into a kind of semi-trance and so on.

– Are you afraid of that? Afraid of losing control?

– I'm a bit used to it, remember? I shrugged. But no, I'm not, provided of course that I trust the person. It's rather manipulative, isn't it?

She paused before answering.

– Quite. This is why I have developed, as hypnotic induction, a combination of therapies with weighty emphasis upon verbal suggestion as well as Freudian free-association techniques. I'm no Erickson disciple; he's largely discredited, precisely for being too manipulative.

– What methods?

– Indirect suggestion, confusion techniques, double binds – never mind. Let me explain how I work. All right?

To my amazement she lit a cigarette and offered me one.

– First I will determine your degree of physical and emotional suggestibility. I will then prepare you for hypnosis by using auto-suggestion and autogenic training. Both processes teach the sub-conscious to believe something for a given purpose. This is accomplished through repetitive, constant self-affirmations. Auto-suggestion may be quickened through mental visualization of what a patient – you – would like to change. It may be regarded as an aspect of prayer, meditation and other similar activities, and is commonly accomplished by presenting the mind with repetitive thoughts, until those thoughts become internalized and trans-muted into actualities.

– Sounds promising, I smiled, rather overwhelmed.

– 'Practice makes perfect' can actually be achieved, Dr Altamira smiled back, in as much as it allows for increased confidence, the conquering of life-long fears, heightened mental faculties, even the eradication of diseases or infections, and has been proven significant in cancer treatment.

– As a kind of mental placebo?

– To some extent. The mechanisms of pathological fixations and obsessions resemble the process of autosuggestion. However, its efficiency is indisputable. The reason why I advocate starting with autogenic training is that the suggestions then originate with *you*, not with *me*. Once we have achieved progress in this field, we can move on to hypnosis in order to modify your emotional content and attitudes, as well as dysfunctional habits, psycho-somatic disorders and, not least, addiction.

Dr Altamira showed me into another room, predictably bathed in a sort of aquarium-light, with the inevitable wave-wind-drum-and-dingaling music I perceive as distasteful. Ironically, it was meant to produce preliminary relaxation.

Nearly two hours of her patience failed to yield the desired results. Hyper-suggestibility, the *sine qua non* condition for this therapy, proved impossible in my case. My mental activity was too great to allow a genuine increase in susceptibility to any suggestion whatsoever. It seems my fascination with the tran-scendental was out of place in the doctor's attempt to get me focused on concrete and practical points.

In actual fact, the problem was of another nature. Instead of concentrating on the task, I could not help but transcribe the experience in my head. I could not let the surroundings fade out, the quintessence of extreme concentration. This I only seem to manage when writing. (While Lisa was staying at my place, for instance, she would turn up the television whenever my neigh-bours played loud music, which was nearly all the time, yet I never heard a thing.) My mental perception remained global, as my mind was taking in every peripheral detail and processing the whole situation into words. My awareness was too acute to be put 'on hold'. Nor did suspension of time set in. Eyes shut or not, the mental blank savoured on the beach was not reproducible.

Not even Dr Altamira's monotonous voice managed to make me sleepy, for it was not an exclusive sound. Consequently, my heartbeat didn't slow down either, as it should have done. I guess I must have been too curious about what I hoped would happen actually to let it happen. (Or was I far too anxious, as in sexual situations?) Instead of surrendering to the flow of the subconscious, I interfered, perhaps resisted, becoming over-conscious instead. In short, my receptivity to mental impressions killed the sensations. I was always twice removed from the first degree. Writing it all down in my mind was a reflex reaction I was unable to block.

I explained all this to Dr Altamira after we returned to her study – but again, as if dictating to myself. It was getting exasperating. Apparently, I was more disappointed than she was.

– You obviously have a 'professional deformation', she quietly remarked. How far into your book are you?

– Too far not to be scared of its implications, privately speaking, should it by some miracle be accepted. I have laid myself bare, even stripped others, and not in a shy way.

– It's a diary, right?

– Yes, but not totally 'quite', as you would say. Still, this is how it started and well, I guess I got carried away.

Her smile encouraged me to pursue my line.

– Ten years ago, in Paris, another manuscript was accepted, but I cringed from having it published. For one thing, I then also feared the personal consequences; for another, I just did not find my writing satisfactory. As French prose tends to be, it was rather long-winded and verbose. Now, however, I feel this could be . . . better than merely okay.

– Would you call this one a *roman à clef*?

– Apart from the fact that the keys are easy to unravel, no. The intention is neither indiscretion nor revelation; it is, though, a personal chronicle, and therefore a tricky proposition, entailing wide breaches of privacy.

– Dr Juan told me about your strained relationship with your mother. I suppose you are worried that, if your book were published, it wouldn't exactly help matters.

– Well, she's a lot more resilient than my companions at the Lugano clinic, or me for that matter. Yet even she would realize that portraits in this narrative do not claim to be X-rays or photographs. But to answer your question, it's my father I would worry about most. He has always considered confidences to be an uncouth form of exhibitionism. Anyway, I sighed, it's all 'wishful worries' for the time being.

– Quite, she smiled again, but pensively. I paint as a hobby and also claim not to represent X-rays or photographs, but in the end, that's what I do, from my biased angle. We always transfigure or transcribe our personal reality, don't we? You come back from a trip with someone and both accounts of it will be honed and tinged by emotional perception. Let's call your book a non-fictional novel, and my pictures non-factual images. What do you think?

– Don't know . . . There is a deprecatory connotation to the term 'faction', as if describing something hybrid, neither fish nor fowl, allowing an author to exonerate indiscretion and defuse opprobrium. I disagree. To me, it renders justice to the kaleido-scopic nature of subjectivity. My story is a mosaic – as are your paintings, I guess.

– Up to a point. From a bird's-eye view, perhaps.

She chuckled while rummaging in her handbag. I didn't get the joke but the funny thing was that, as she sprayed herself with a familiar scent, I had no emotional reaction whatsoever: hitherto, recognizing my mother's perfume had filled me with discomfort. It had struck me, talking to Dr Altamira, that all trace of anger towards my mother seemed to have dissolved when discussing her.

Was that, along with the fact that I didn't seem to be able to lie any more, the delayed benefits of therapy Dottore M had predicted? Had anger been my main problem all along? At myself for, among other things, feeling that way about her? At whoever caused the pain of rejection or betrayal? Would this finally explain my aggressiveness when drinking too much? With the ebbing of anger, hadn't the need to numb it become obsolete?

– I pray this to be true, I whispered.

– It probably is, the *doctora* declared. As to lying, mind you, she smiled with a twinkle in her eye, what you experience is natural but short-lived. In the aftermath of intense therapy even compulsive liars swing over to the extreme of relentless sincerity. It has become a habit. Resuming social life soon snaps you out of it. Recent studies concur upon establishing that we all lie an average of 2.93 times during a ten-minute span, overwhelmingly for convenience or out of altruism, i.e. to make life easier for oneself and others. Lies meant to hurt or cheat are the exception. For your information (another wink), depressive subjects lie far less, their perception of reality too heightened to allow them to fool themselves, and not for their own good. Call it excessive lucidity. You are inclined to poetry. Lying will come back as a natural survival mechanism in no time.

She chuckled again, powdering her nose.

– I must go for lunch. Right. On the basis of your goodwill, this is what I suggest: you finish your book. I well know one could spend a lifetime retouching the same canvas, but try to stop before overkill. Then *you make a pause*. This is crucial for you, mentally and physically. You look awful, Aleana, I'm sorry to say. Give yourself a two-week break, wind down and come to see me again after the first week – if you wish, that is.

– Very much, I answered, full of gratitude for her patience and for the warm conversation.

In fact, I envied the one having lunch with her. She was an original, kindred spirit, and fun too.

– One last thing, she said, struggling with her tight belt: do you really wish your book to be published?

I sensed this was no casual afterthought, and struggled with my answer. It had to be a yes or a no.

– I do, I finally said, as solemnly as if in front of an altar, sounding a bit silly too.

– Glad to hear it, because I'll tell you what: should you get the chance, go for it. You might not be given a second opportunity to publish a first book. Meanwhile, choose one sentence you repeat over and again until falling asleep. It might do you good.

I lay in bed that night, and the three following nights, reiterating ad infinitum, 'My manuscript will be accepted, my manuscript will be accepted, my manuscript will be accepted, my manuscript will be accepted . . . '

Yesterday, I found a message on the answering machine. It was Naim Attallah, effervescent as is his wont, announcing he wanted to publish my book and was awaiting the last chapter *verrrrrry* urgently.

I jumped up and down till out of breath. Wow! Christ! Hurrah! In fact I couldn't believe it until I had replayed the message several times. Was this the power of incantation and the miracle of self-fulfilling prophecies? I resolved there and then to keep sticking to Dr Altamira's formula, just in case.

The feeling of having 'arrived in port', of achieving a goal thanks to relentless and regular hard work, is elating. I have only too seldom experienced it. Had I continued drinking as before, I would never have been able for the past two months to follow through the rhythm.

Having calmed down, I called Naim. He insisted I use my real name for authorship. Fair enough, since even the most modest promotion would be bound to reveal it.

I have not prefaced this book with the customary 'any resemblances to existing people are purely coincidental, etc.' There's a limit to bullshit. I am no Imperial Highness, Prince Michael Alexandrovitch Dmitry Obolensky Romanoff (alias Harry F. Ferguson of Chicago, a mobster turned into one of Hollywood's darlings), of whom David Niven recalls that 'depending on whom he talked to and his estimate of their gullibility, he operated a sliding scale of claims to kinship to the murdered Czar, and that it fluctuated wildly'.

Naim laughed. I went insistently.

– I have called myself Aleana and stand by the viewpoint that, this text having been written as a relief, a catharsis and a pleasure, I'd like to stick to that name in *my* version of *my* story. Would you agree?

He did.

Having hung up and fluttered some more, my mood suddenly swerved into anguish. Was it interesting to others, after all? Was my English good enough? Would I be 'held hostage by the beholders of my secrets', or ostracized by others?

The anguish abated no sooner than I sat down to write this last chapter. It started with:

'Our eyes are filters and magnifying glasses. Our capacity to sort out the abundance of feelings depends on delicate imponderables. We twist and distort, we lie when not aware of it, or vice versa. We imagine, select, embroider and omit. We do what we can to find our way in the plethora of experiences and the labyrinth of emotions, full of gaps and fragments as they are. With the help of words, we sketch changing maps of our search for significance, and make it tantalizing.

'In the beginning was the Verb, but "language can only deal meaningfully with a special, restricted segment of reality. The rest, and it is probably the much larger part, is silence," wrote George Steiner. He trusts our verbal ability to guide another through our innermost doors, and to open his own. Hence his axiomatic: "Hope is grammatical."

'In my less authoritative opinion, words constantly thrust forward the magnet that summons them, and us, into life. Life is a movie we endlessly edit, subtitle and synchronize. Language creates the marvellous freedom to do so.'